HISTORY TIMELINES

Ancient Egypt

FRANCIS NASH

SIMON & SCHUSTER
EDUCATION

CONTENTS

INTRODUCTION

TIMELINES is a series of photocopiable resources to help teach history at Key Stage 2, covering the most popular options in the Programme of Study. Each book has an historical introduction, a time line, and about 28 units dealing with a wide variety of topics. Each unit has background historical information for the teacher and one or more pages for the pupil which may be photocopied and used as appropriate.

The Timelines

Each book in the series contains a time line – a basic chronological structure for the events and trends of the topic. We have put some basic dates and information on to the time line, together with some little pictures to stick on in the right places. Many of the activities fit onto the timeline: children may cut out, colour or adapt the pictures and stick them in the right places, and gradually build up a picture of the whole period, with an idea of what happened when, when things were invented, and what came in which order. This is a fairly simple way of developing the concept of chronology, essential to the understanding of history, to the ideas of *change* and *cause*, and the core of National Curriculum Attainment Target 1: Knowledge and understanding of history.

However the use of the time line is not essential to the book, and you may equally well use the materials to help with a project book or folder. Many are planned to save laborious copying or preparation, without taking away the opportunity to do constructive work.

The Activity Sheets and levels of difficulty

We have tried to offer as wide a variety as possible of activities. They may be used for individual, pair or class work. They are not meant to be worked through methodically, and may be done in any order.

We are aware that this topic is tackled at a wide variety of ages, sometimes at the beginning of Key Stage 2 in conjunction with Ancient Greece, and sometimes towards the end. We have tried to include material for all ages and relevant levels of difficulty. Wherever possible we have tried to devise open-ended activities which can be tackled according to the age and ability of the child – activities for

example which ask for writing, which can be responded to very briefly or in greater detail. We have also put in separately some very simple activitities, and some more challenging ones which cater to higher level statements of attainment.

Teaching about Ancient Egypt

This is not intended, of course, to be the sole resource for teaching the topic. We have assumed in preparing this book that there will be other sources of information and work – in particular information books and perhaps text books. The activities here are intended to complement your other sources, whatever they are. We have not therefore put much basic information on the pupil pages, and we have tried to offer variety rather than repeat what is easily available elsewhere. We have also provided quite a lot of background information on each topic for the teacher – information which is not necessarily available in information books, and which will save time and effort for yourselves. We hope you will find this useful.

The topics

We have tried to include a good mixture of topics – not only pyramids, temples, gods and pharaohs but also social topics such as childhood. We have attempted to provide topics which link with other National Curriculum history topics which you may be doing – in particular the study of themes over a long period of time.

Historical issues

Change. Most of Egyptian rule, culture, and daily life changed remarkably little over a very long period of time, after a time of rapid development in the Old Kingdom. The pharaohs' power rose and fell over the centuries, but essentially the position was the same over 3000 years; compare that with the last 3000 years of European history. Building styles, art and architecture were almost unchanged after the 'rules' and methods had been established early on. Agriculture and daily life for the masses was the same almost until 1960 AD, when the Aswan dam was built. Technological development was almost nil, apart from the wheels and horses and other things brought by the Hyksos in c.1500 BC.

It is interesting to compare this with the changes in recent modern history, and even in the lifetimes of children, when there is always something new and changing in technology, fashion, daily life, food, and so on, and ask why the rate of change is so different. Why was it so slow then, and why so fast now? Possible reasons for the Egyptian slowness to change are: the relative isolation of the country from its neighbours; lack of internal competition, since everything was owned by the pharaoh and run by his officials; Egyptian feelings of superiority over foreigners; the stable climate and normal comfortable surplus of food; the narrowness of the country and simplicity of transport i.e. up, down and across the river; perhaps the complexity of their writing and number systems.

Questions of change are covered in NC AT 1, Levels 3,4,5.

Evidence. Most of the evidence for Egyptian life come from tombs - manuscripts, pictures, things left for use in the afterlife. This is much narrower of course than in modern history. It is worth asking whether this leads to distortion - for example, whether the Egyptians were not so concerned with death and burial after all, or whether the evidence is mainly to do with the rich and powerful (as it usually has been until recent history), or whether the picture of life we have is better than it really was because they avoided dwelling on unpleasant realities.

The other point to make about evidence is that most of it comes from Middle and Upper Egypt, where it is dryer and hotter, and much less from the Delta, where the high water table and damper climate has meant that much of the evidence has gone - but where most of the people lived. This is especially relevant when the capital of the country was moved into the Delta, in the Late Period. So perhaps there is more emphasis on the south, and on earlier periods, than there ought to be.

These points of evidence are covered in AT 2 Level 4 and AT 3.

Origins

Before about 10,000 BC most of North Africa was fertile grassland, inhabited by nomads and hunters. But towards the end of this period the climate gradually changed and the grassland turned into desert. Only the great River Nile flowed through this desert, and the people who had been spread out over North Africa moved increasingly to the Nile and began to settle and farm there.

The Nile provided the perfect conditions for civilisation. The river's annual flood fertilised the 'black land' alongside its banks and allowed farmers to produce in most years more than enough to feed the population, which meant that part of the labour force could be diverted to tasks which were more than just staying alive. It meant that there could be craft workers, officials, and so on. Near the river and in the desert to the east was a good supply of building stone – granite, limestone and sandstone – and also gold. The Nile provided a safe form of transport, which helped carry goods from one part to another, and also made it easy for officials to administer the country. It was fairly remote from other vigorous civilisations, being surrounded by desert and the sea, which made it safe and stable, but close enough for some ideas to pass from the older civilisations in Mesopotamia – in particular writing.

Early Dynastic Period
2920-2575 BC (Dynasties 1 – 3)

Egyptian kings are organised by historians into dynasties, and periods are usually referred to not by date but by dynasty; e.g. Tutankhamun was an 18th dynasty pharaoh. The divisions between periods are not at all clear-cut, and the dates here are fairly approximate, especially during the First and Second Intermediate Periods.

Egypt is believed to have been united into one kingdom under Menes (the name is not known for certain) in c.2920 BC. Before this there were probably two kingdoms, Upper (South) and Lower (North) Egypt.

In this period *writing* came into use; the idea came from Sumeria but the Egyptians developed their own hieroglyphic system from scratch.

Memphis, roughly on the border of Upper and Lower Egypt, became the capital of the kingdom. In later years the capital often changed to other places, but Memphis was always an important religious and government centre.

In this period the rich and powerful were buried in mastabas, large low rectangular brick tombs.

The first *pyramid* was started for the 3rd dynasty king Djoser, designed by Imhotep – the Step Pyramid at Saqqara. It was built in c.2600 BC.

Towns began to grow, and people began to build mud-brick houses (this was possible because it rained so rarely) instead of reed huts to live in.

Old Kingdom
2575-2134 BC (Dynasties 4-8)

In this period Egyptian civilisation reached its height, and art, architecture, administration, medicine and mathematics all flourished. Many of the customs and artefacts which we think of as Egyptian were developed in this period and remained more or less unchanged for 2000 years.

The 4th dynasty saw the building of the vast pyramids at Giza, by the kings Khufu (the Great Pyramid), Khephren and Menkaure. They took about 20 years each to build, with 50-100,000 men working on them at peak times during the flood season. Never again were such huge buildings constructed.

The king was equated with the sun god Re, and reached the height of absolute power. The southern border was established at Aswan. There were great expeditions to Nubia (Sudan) and Punt (Somalia).

The 6th dynasty king Pepy II is believed to have ruled for 94 years – the longest reign of any monarch in the world. But towards the end of this period the power of the king began to decline. He became regarded as the son of Re rather than Re himself. The central authority of the kingdom was gradually lost. There was a series of poor floods, famine, and civil war.

First Intermediate Period
2134-2040 BC (Dynasties 9-11)

Egypt was divided in two and nominally ruled by different dynasties, one at Herakleopolis and one at Thebes,though neither probably had much power. There was general poverty, and no great works of art or building.

Writings from the time describe the situation: 'The officials are murdered and their papers seized....The wrongdoer is everywhere. A man takes his shield when he goes to plough.Men sit in the bushes until the traveller comes, in order to plunder his load. The robber has riches....He who possessed no property is now a man of wealth. The poor man is full of joy. The owners of robes are now in rags. The children of princes are dashed against the walls....All happiness has disappeared, the land is bowed down in misery.'

Middle Kingdom
2040-1640 BC
(Dynasties 11-14)

Mentuhotpe reunited the country with the capital at Thebes, and Egypt again entered a period of prosperity and expansion. The Middle Kingdom reached its height in the 12th dynasty under Senwosret III (1878-41 BC), who conquered Nubia, built forts there and extended Egypt's southern border south to the Second Cataract to include much of Nubia. He also led expeditions to Palestine and increased Egyptian influence there. At home the power of the pharaoh increased again, and there was more building of temples and sculpture, though pyramids were no longer used as burial places. The capital was moved again to Memphis.

In the 13th dynasty there were about 70 kings in 140 years, but Egypt stayed strong. Perhaps the real power was held by the vizier (chief minister) and high officials.

Second Intermediate Period
1640-1532 BC
(Dynasties 15-17)

This is an obscure period in Egyptian history. There are not many reliable records of what happened. The 13th and 14th dynasties disappeared into historical vagueness. Asian immigrants moved into the Delta, and from them a new ruling class called the Hyksos ('rulers of foreign lands') claimed the kingdom of Egypt. They set up a new capital at Avaris, in the Delta, and gradually spread their control over the whole country.

The Hyksos did not try to impose a foreign culture on Egypt, however; they had themselves crowned as pharaohs, wrote their names in hieroglyphics, and used Egyptian officials and methods in their rule.

This was the first time that Egypt had been conquered or ruled by foreigners, and it led to considerable innovations in this very conservative country. The wheel came into use for the first time, with the horse-drawn chariots used by the Hyksos for fighting; also new kinds of bow, scimitar and armour; new animals (the zebu), crops, technology (for weaving and metal-working), musical instruments and dances.

With the 17th dynasty, a native Egyptian one based at Thebes, which had previously accepted the Hyksos as overlords, a struggle for independence began which was finally successful in about 1532 BC. Egypt was again reunited under Egyptian rulers.

New Kingdom 1550-1070 BC
(Dynasties 18-20)

This period was the last golden age of Egyptian history. It was also a time of expansion of trade and empire, from Kush in the south to Syria in the north. Trading links were established with Mycenae, Crete and Cyprus as well as Palestine and Africa to the South.

The Egyptian Empire reached its height under Tuthmosis I (1504-1492 BC), who conquered Nubia and turned it into a colony ruled direct from Egypt, and reached the Euphrates in the north, Palestine and Syria becoming self-governing areas acknowledging Egypt as overlord. Egypt had a large standing army for the first time. Wealth poured in from the empire and there was a burst of building of temples and great statues. Egypt became less insular; more Egyptians travelled and lived abroad, and more foreigners came to live in Egypt, especially in the Delta.

Other notable rulers of the 18th dynasty included Hatsheput, the first powerful woman to rule successfully in her own right in a time of peace and prosperity; and Akhenaten, an extraordinary figure who with his famous wife Nefertiti set up Aten, the sun-god, as the only god, forbade the worship of all the other gods and ordered their monuments to be scrapped, built a brand-new capital at El-Amarna, and started a kind of cultural revolution in art and society, reflected in a more informal life-style and dress. But under his son Tutunkhamun, of the famous tomb, this revolution was reversed and things returned very much to normal.

The great ruler of the 19th dynasty was Ramesses II (1290-1224 BC), who built more buildings and colossal statues than any other king. He was a self-glorified leader, deified in his lifetime, and engaged in large expeditions against the Hittites (north Syria) and Mitanni (north Iraq). He had 150 children by large numbers of wives and concubines, and moved the capital to the Delta, which unfortunately means that there is relatively less detailed information about Egyptian history after this as the damp Delta with its high water table preserves far less than the dry climate to the south.

After this again there was a long period of slow decline. The empire to the north and south was gradually lost. The Sea-people, an alliance of Libyans and other Eastern Mediterraneans, attacked Egypt twice and were defeated both times; the second time they were trapped in nets in the Delta and slaughtered. But this was a short-lived success. The pharaohs became less powerful and the priests and temples more so, so that the southern half of the country became a virtually independent state ruled from the temple of Amun at Thebes. Grave-robbing became frequent - perhaps because of poverty or non-payment of workers.

This was the end of Egypt as a major international power. Although the pharaohs nominally lasted another thousand years, they never again held the same power, and Egypt lost its pre-eminent position in the ancient world for good.

Third Intermediate Period
1070-712 BC (Dynasties 21-25)

This is a confused period. Egypt was divided all through this time, with the South ruling itself separately under the high priests of Thebes. The 22nd Dynasty was Libyan, ruling from the Delta; dynasties 22 to 25 all ruled different parts of Egypt simultaneously. In about 730 BC the 25th dynasty, from Nubia, tried to conquer the whole country with a big expedition north to Memphis, but only partly succeeded.

Late Period
712-332 BC (Dynasties 25-30)

Egypt's isolation was ended, and she became one power among a number in the Middle East, and not a very strong one. The Nubians completed their domination of the country, took on Egyptian rites and habits, and emphasised old traditions, with a return to Old and Middle Kingdom sources.

In 671 BC the Assyrians conquered Egypt, and in 663 BC they sacked and burned Thebes. In 653 BC they were expelled again, and Egypt turned to a system of alliances with other powers to keep out her enemies. There were more and more foreign troops and traders in Egypt - Greeks, Nubians, Libyans, Phonecians,

Syrians and Jews - displaced by the rapid rise and fall of the Assyrian Empire.

The Greeks provided the first proper Egyptian navy and helped open new trade routes, and Egypt allied itself with them as a protection against the growing Persian Empire. A Greek trading base was built at Naukritis in the Delta, and other settlements sprang up. Egyptian interpreters showed Greek intellectuals round their shrines; the Greeks were fascinated by this great civilisation of the past and fallaciously traced their own history and culture back to Egypt.

Economically Egypt was not as successful as before. Perhaps their lack of coinage did not help them in trading. They had to import iron, which they paid for with their grain surplus.

In 525 the Persians did invade, and Egypt quickly succumbed. Although the Persian rulers took on the title of pharaoh they governed Egypt as a colony, which the Egyptians bitterly resented. After a long period of resistance, in which they were helped by the Greeks in return for grain, the Persians were expelled, and there followed a new period of peace and prosperity, until Alexander the Great took the country in 332 BC.

The Ptolemies

The Ptolemies were the last pharaohs, though they were Greek and Greek-speaking. Alexander died suddenly in 323 BC, after starting the building of Alexandria, the greatest city of the Greek world. Ptolemy I, a general from Macedonia, inherited Egypt as his share of Alexander's empire, and his descendents ruled for the next 250 years.

Although the Ptolemies were Greek they ruled Egypt as a separate country, and even took steps towards building a new empire, with expeditions into Palestine and Nubia. They also held Cyprus for a time, and some other islands. Egyptian traditions were restored and emphasised, though Egypt was now a part of the Greek world.

In 30 BC, with the death of Cleopatra, Egypt became a Roman colony, part of that growing empire. The Romans ruled the country for what they could get out of it - in particular its grain. The 3000 year rule of the pharaohs came to an end.

TIMELINE

EGYPT

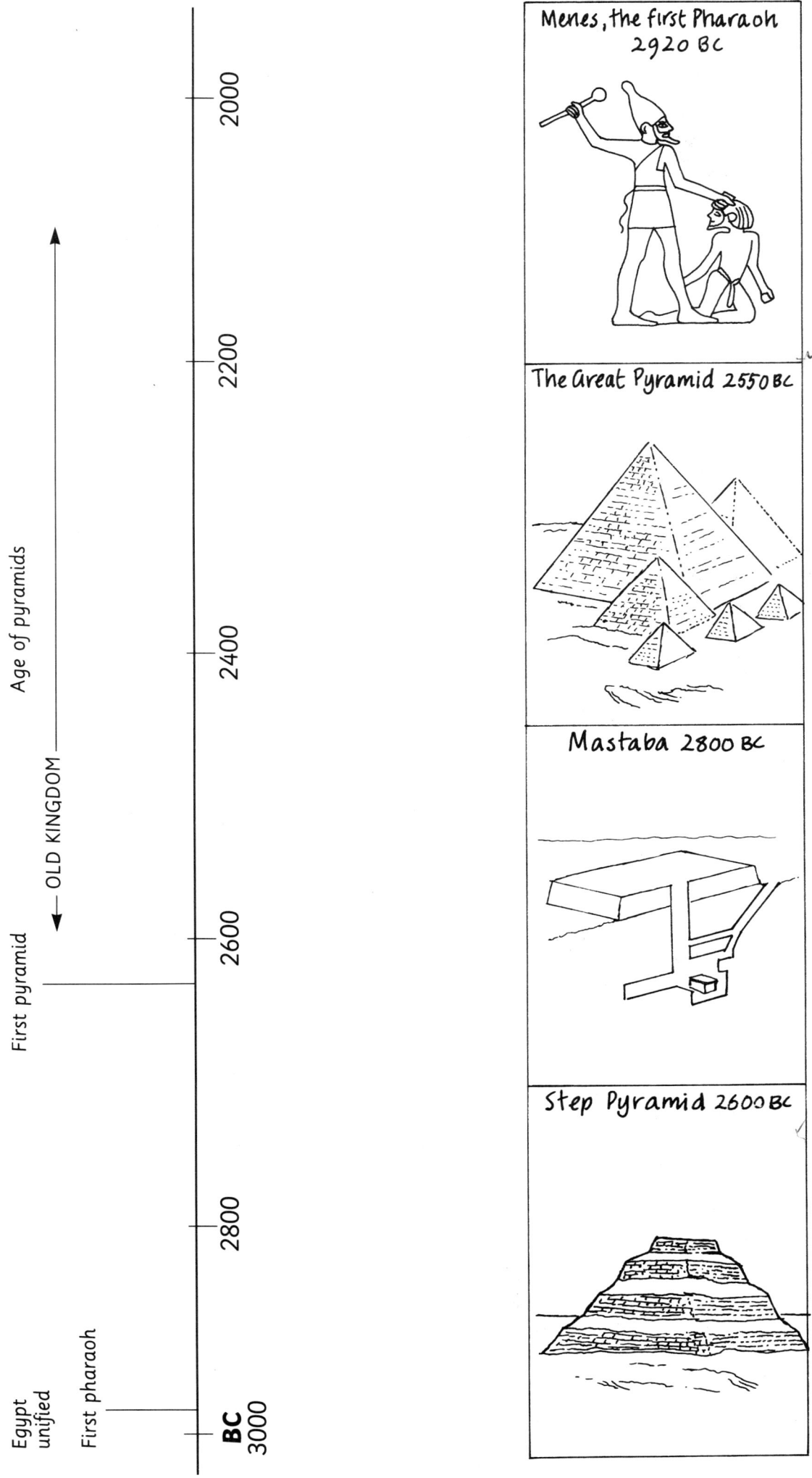

| | Step Pyramid 2600 BC | Mastaba 2800 BC | The Great Pyramid 2550 BC | Menes, the first Pharaoh 2920 BC |

Egypt unified

First pharaoh

First pyramid

Age of pyramids

◄— OLD KINGDOM —►

BC 3000 — 2800 — 2600 — 2400 — 2200 — 2000

TIMELINE 2

EGYPT

Last pyramid built

MIDDLE KINGDOM

Rule of Hyksos

NEW KINGDOM

Egyptian Empire

Egypt divided

2000   1800   1600   1400   1200   1000

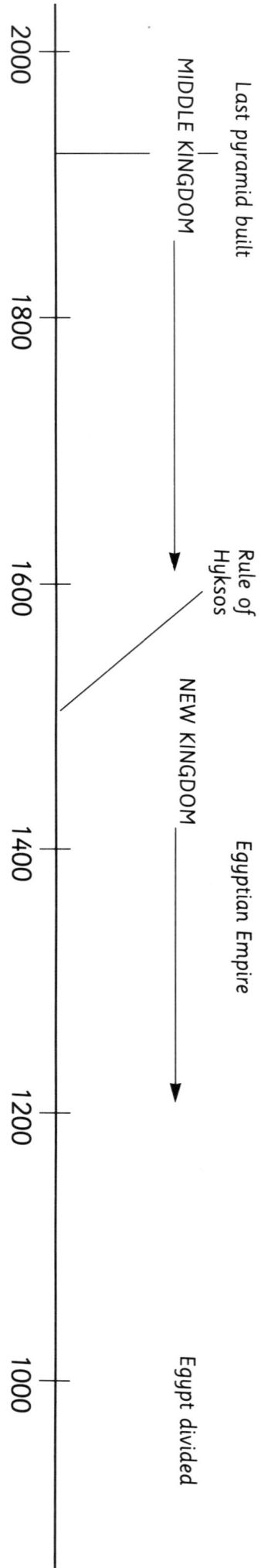

Queen Nefertiti 1340 BC

Chariot 500 BC

Temple 1700 BC

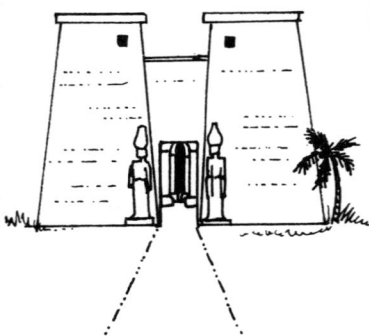

Ramesses II 1290 BC

TIMELINE 3

EGYPT

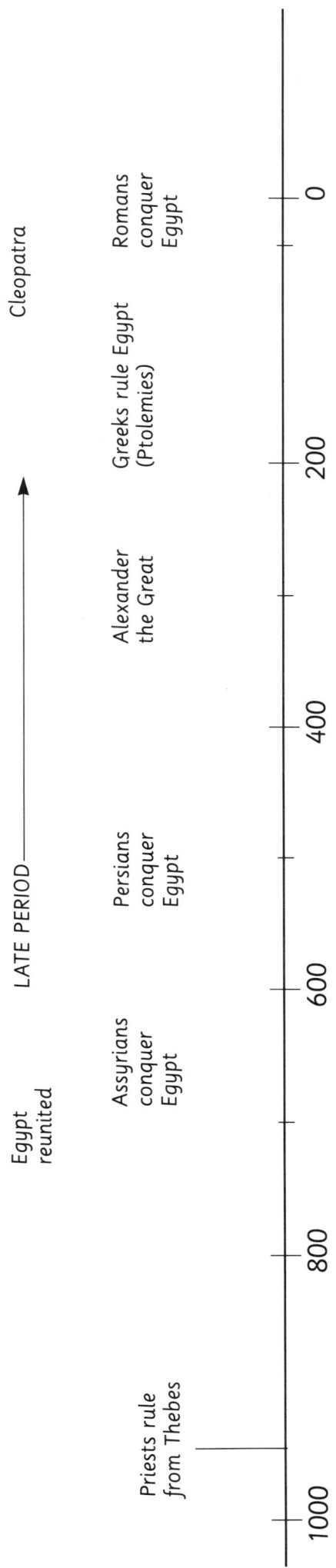

Priests rule from Thebes

Egypt reunited

LATE PERIOD ⟶

Assyrians conquer Egypt

Persians conquer Egypt

Alexander the Great

Greeks rule Egypt (Ptolemies)

Cleopatra

Romans conquer Egypt

1000　800　600　400　200　0

Cleopatra　30 BC

Alexander the Great　330 BC

Roman Soldier　0 BC

Ship　500 BC

≋ WHERE IS EGYPT? ≋

Background

This basic map is to help give an idea of where Egypt is in relation to Britain and the rest of Europe. It can be used either for information only or for some mapwork relating geographical skills to history.

✏ Activities

Colour the sea blue; Egypt red; the north African desert yellow; other land as you wish (perhaps green).

Using scale

How far is it fron Egypt to Britain (in a straight line)? To Italy? To Greece? Which country is nearest and which furthest?

In the ancient world you would not travel by plane but by ship or over land. If you were going from Egypt to Greece or Rome, how would you go, and how long do you think it would take, if you went 50 miles a day by sea, or 20 miles by land? You coud plot the journey on the map.

Which places do you think were most important to Egypt?

Using co-ordinates

Which place is at B2 on your map?

Which at C3?

What is the co-ordinate for Egypt?

For discussion

Draw attention to Greece and Rome, and to the areas nearest Egypt – Syria/Palestine, the land to the south of Egypt, the desert to the west. Try to connect Egypt's history with its geographical place (land battles and empire to the north, south and east; trade by sea with Crete and Greece; north and west Europe not important; Britain probably not even heard of).

Attainment targets:
History AT 1 level 2, 3;
Geography AT 1 level 2, 3, 4

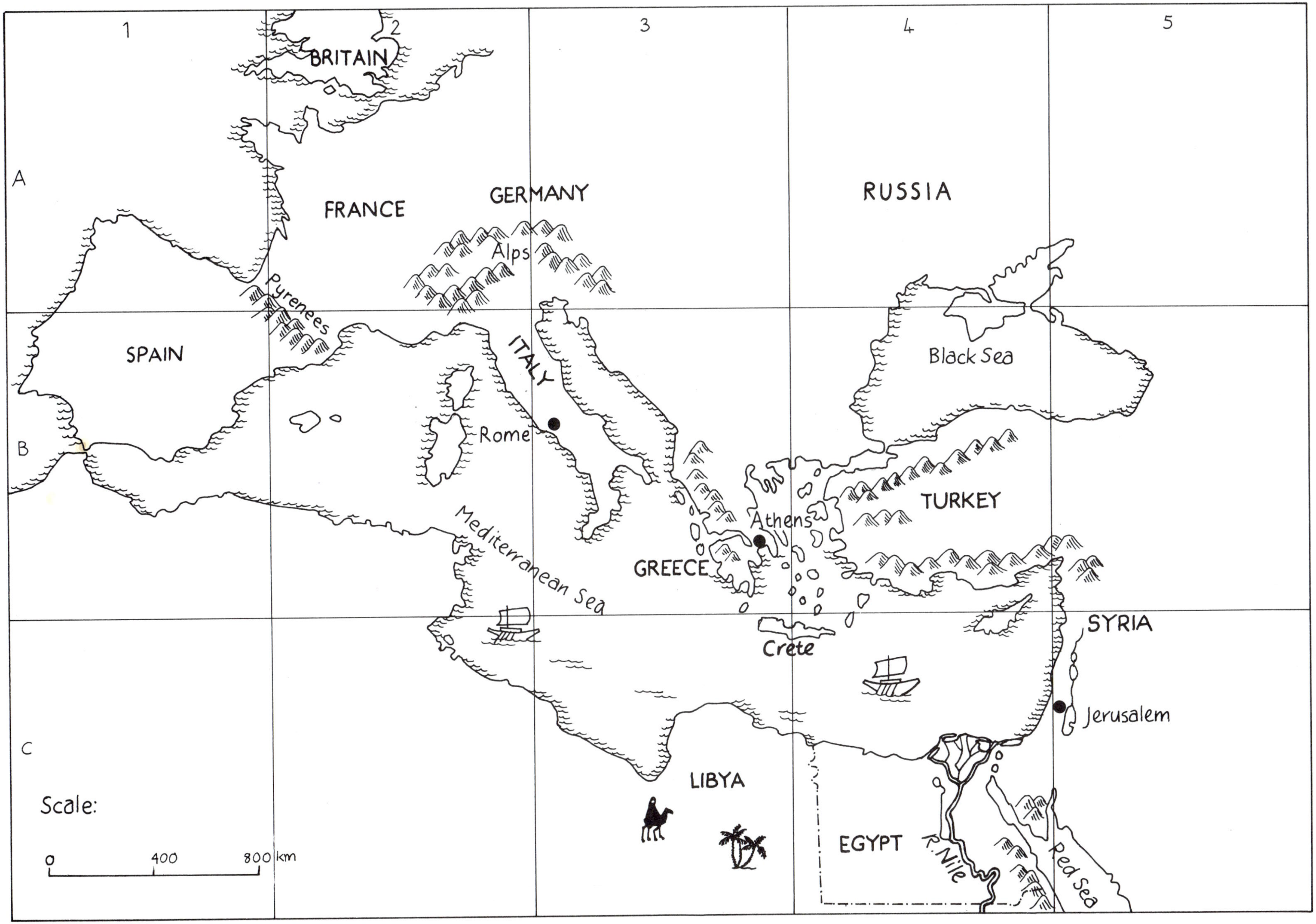
1
2
3
4
5
A
B
C
BRITAIN
FRANCE
GERMANY
RUSSIA
Alps
Pyrenees
SPAIN
ITALY
Rome
Black Sea
TURKEY
Athens
GREECE
Mediterranean Sea
Crete
SYRIA
Jerusalem
LIBYA
EGYPT
R. Nile
Red Sea
Scale:
0
400
800 km

☞ ANCIENT EGYPT ☜

Background

The important part of Ancient Egypt consisted almost entirely of the River Nile and the land on its banks. The traditional boundary was at the First Cataract (now just north of the Aswan Dam). From here to the Delta was called Upper Egypt; from the Delta to the sea was called Lower Egypt. The capital moved from place to place during the 3000 years; at first it was at Memphis, just south of modern Cairo, conveniently sited where Upper and Lower Egypt met; at other times it was at Thebes, in the south, and later on at various places in the Delta. Almost the entire population (about 4 million at most) lived very near the Nile and relied on it for their living.

West of the Nile were the sandhills of the Libyan desert, with a few oases fed underground from the Nile. East was a range of high mountains (up to 2000 m), which were less barren then and supported some farming and grazing. There were important mineral mines there – copper, tin, stone for building, semi-precious stones – and also routes to the Red Sea.

Egypt was a self-contained and quite isolated place. It relied on its own agriculture. Its people were surrounded by desert. To the south was Nubia, which provided Egypt with gold, wood, spices, ivory, ebony and wild animals. Egypt conquered part of Nubia for a while and later was conquered in turn. To the north, by sea, was the Mediterranean coast of Palestine and Syria, where they got timber (there were not many trees in Egypt, so this was important), wine and oil, and some minerals in exchange for gold and food.

✎ Activities

A base map of Egypt. The fertile areas should be coloured green, the desert yellow, the mountains brown. Other features can of course be added as you wish.

Emphasise the importance of the Nile, the land which could be cultivated, how cut off they were from other inhabited places; why roads were not really necessary (which explains why they did not use wheels for so long?).

Use the scale to work out how long it would take to travel by river from one end of the country to the other, for an official of the Pharaoh, going perhaps 30 miles a day.

Attainment targets:
History AT 1
Geography AT 1 levels 3,4

ANCIENT EGYPT

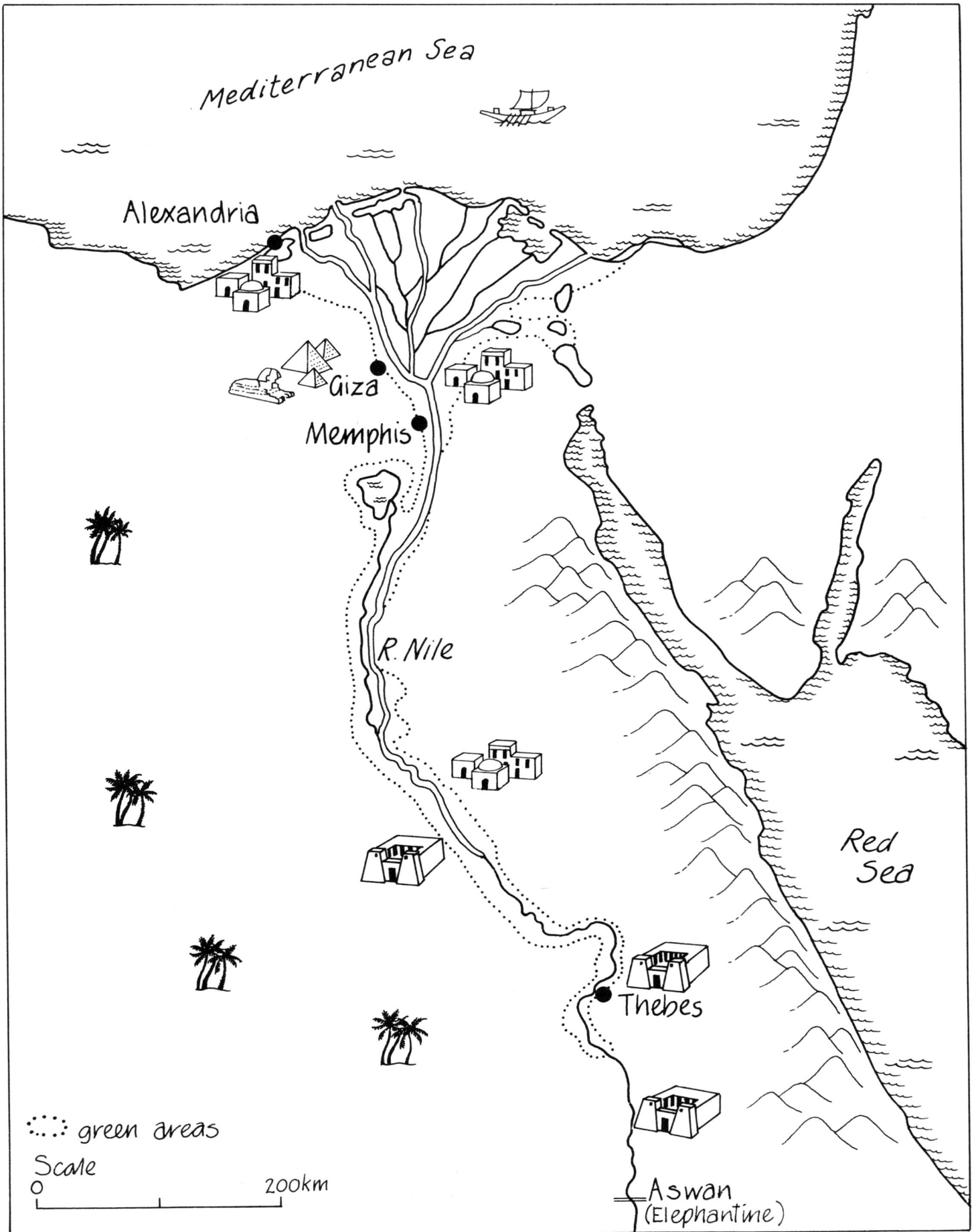

Mediterranean Sea

Alexandria

Giza

Memphis

R. Nile

Red Sea

Thebes

:::: green areas

Scale

0   200km

Aswan
(Elephantine)

Background

The Nile starts 4,145 miles from the Mediterranean at Lake Victoria, but only the last 900 miles run through Egypt. South of Aswan there are six cataracts – rushing, rocky passages of water that are difficult to navigate. From the First Cataract to the Delta the Nile runs smoothly for 650 miles, through a valley 2 - 12 miles wide bordered by limestone cliffs. For the last 250 miles the river breaks into lots of waterways which make up the Nile Delta.

Egypt's land was watered and fertilised by the inundation, or flooding, of the Nile, which took place every summer and was caused by the rains from the Ethiopian summer monsoon. (The Egyptians said that a tear from the goddess Isis made the river rise.) The water began to rise in late June and reached the top of its flood in August - September, when the whole of the valley, from cliff to cliff, was a sea dotted by the odd island village protected by dykes and banks. The flood was about 6 - 9 metres above its usual height and was regular and predictable, only very occasionally failing or rising to exceptional levels.

In October the flood subsided and left a thick layer of rich black earth over the land. The farmers cleared out the canals and ditches, restored landmarks and marked out fields, and planted their crops for harvest in January - April. From April to June the fields dried out and the Nile reached its lowest level.

The Delta was swampier and harder to cultivate. There were meadows, gardens, vinyards and marshes for hunting, fishing and reed-cropping.

Egyptian farmers were happier than most. There was less risk of drought or disaster. They worshipped the flood as a god – a bearded god called Hapy with a cluster of water-plants on his head. An Egyptian hymn is reproduced in the panel on the right.

Hundreds of thousands of years of the annual flooding of the Nile, and thousands of years of traditional Egyptian farming dependant on it, came to an end when the Aswan Dam was built in 1960.

Hail O Nile, who issues forth from the earth, who comes to give life to the people of Egypt...

Praised by his followers whose fields you water.

Created by Re to give life to all who thirst.

Who lets the desert drink with streams descending from heaven.

Beloved of the earth-god, controller of the corn-god...

Lord of fish who causes the water-fowl to sail upstream...

Who makes barley and creates wheat so that temples celebrate...

When the Nile overflows, offerings are made to you, cattle are slaughtered for you, birds are fattened for you, desert lions are trapped for you that your goodness be repaid.

"Its fields are full of good things and it has provision for every day. Its granaries overflow...they reach the sky. Its ponds are full of fishes and its lakes of birds. Its fields are green with grass and its banks bear dates. He who lives there is happy and the poor man is like the great elsewhere."

Flood:
"The entire valley was like the sea. All people were as water birds or swimmers in a torrent...all the temples were like marshes."

Famine:
"The entire south died of hunger, every man devouring his own children."

Flood! is a simple game intended to give players some idea of the farmer' dependence on the river, and its risks.

Discussion points that could come out of it are

▲ Their welfare depends entirely on nature, and there is very little they can do about it (compare with today);

▲ Mostly things were all right, and farmers were pretty lucky; but

▲ There was always an element of risk – you never know year to year what actually is going to happen.

Suggest that children colour good years green and bad years red. Compare their results to see whether some have fared better than others.

〰〰〰〰〰〰 FLOOD! 〰〰〰〰〰

You need 2 dice.

You are a farmer on the banks of the River Nile. In the fields you grow wheat for bread and barley for beer, for yourself and your family, and for Pharaoh and his servants. In your garden you grow vegetables and fruit. Each year the river floods. If the flood is too high your house and garden will be washed away and your animals drowned. If the flood is too low the land will be dry and you will not be able to grow enough food for yourselves.

But if the flood is not too low and not too high, you will be able to grow plenty of food for your family, enough to send to Pharaoh's store, and have some left over to swap in the market for other things that you want.

HOW TO PLAY

You are to keep a diary for 10 years about the flood and what happens to you. Roll the dice and add them together to see how much the Nile rises each year.

If things go wrong, try to think what you could do about it -- ask the Pharaoh's officers for help, or say a prayer to the God of the Nile! Red was an unlucky colour for the Egyptians, so you could colour in red for the bad years!

Score	Flood Rise	What Happens
2	under 6 metres	Very low! Crops fail! Nothing to eat, unless you had some in store! Starvation! Will the Pharaoh help?
3,4	6 metres	Low. Poor crops! Not enought to eat! Hunger!
5,6,7,8	7 metres	Just right. Good crops. Enough food. Happiness.
9,10	8 metres	Wonderful! Plenty of food, more than enough for everyone and some to store for next year too!
11	8.5 metres	Watch out! Very high. Make sure the banks round your house are strong enough.
12	9 metres	Flood! Disaster! Banks burst, houses and gardens flooded, animals drown! What can I do?

≋ FLOOD! ≋ Your Diary ≋

YEAR	DICE	FLOOD RISE	WHAT HAPPENS TO YOU . . .
1			
2			
3			
4			
5			
6			
7			
8			
9			
10			

 # FARMING

Background

The farmer's life in Egypt was less desperate than most. He did not have to rely on rainfall, which might fail, but on the flood, which was regular, predictable and mostly dependable. The annual flood also meant a rich and naturally fertilised land. The result of this happy situation was a fairly regular surplus of food, which made possible the enormous labour on the great building projects, the trade of food for desirable imports, and Egyptian civilisation as a whole.

The farming year was divided into ploughing, sowing and reaping. In the autumn (Peret), after the inundation had subsided, they cleared the canals and ditches, ploughed, and planted the crops. In spring (Shemu) they harvested. This was done by the end of May. In May and June the fields lay fallow, and from July to October (Akhet) they were flooded. So in the summer, if they were unlucky, the farmworkers were available for building or other work without affecting the supply of food.

The main crops were emmer (a kind of wheat) for bread; barley, for bread but also for beer; flax for clothes, sails and ropes; and of course papyrus, in the marshes.

The basic tools were a simple hoe or forked stick; a plough drawn by oxen or donkeys; and wooden sickles with flint teeth. The straw from the harvest was used for bedding, thatching and brickmaking.

Farm animals were poultry, oxen, sheep, goats, pigs and donkeys. Some cattle were farmed in herds on the edge of the desert, mostly in the Delta.

✏ Activities

The pictures show the farmer's tasks during each of the three seasons. You could discuss the pictures and ask them to write something about each of them. This could of course range from one-word summaries to detailed descriptions.

Picture 1 shows a variety of autumn tasks – chopping down trees, hoeing, sowing corn, ploughing.

Questions:

How many different things can you spot going on? What sort of tools have they got for hoeing, ploughing? How did they sow? What sort of animals did they use to help them plough? What do you think the squiggly line through the picture is?

Picture 2 shows the harvest.

Questions:

Did men and women both do the harvest? How did they do it? What tools did they use? What did they pick up the wheat in? What do you think they had to do next?

Picture 3 shows a fishing scene. They fished with fish hooks, and also with nets. During the inundation there was of course little for the farmer to do on the land, but fish was an important part of the staple diet.

Questions:

What does the man do with the fish when he has caught them? What is he holding in his hand, and what for?

Attainment targets:
AT 2 level 4;
AT 3 levels 1,2,3,4

THE FARMING YEAR

AUTUMN (PERET)

FLOOD (AKHET)

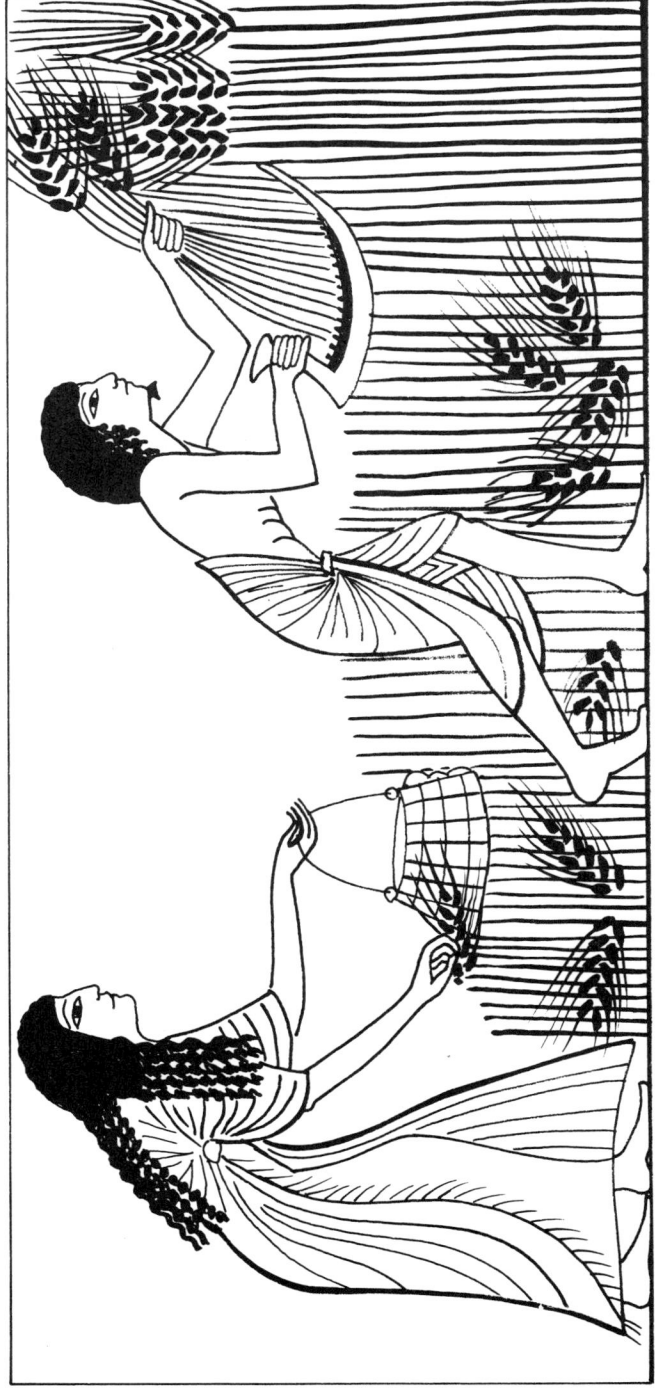

SPRING (SHEMU)

FOOD

The basic Egyptian diet was bread, beer, vegetables, and fresh or dried fish. Even the poor ate this, with some of the fruit and meat below for feasts.

Vegetables: leeks, onions, cucumber, lettuce, garlic, beans, lentils, gourds

Fruit: figs, dates, melons, grapes

Meat (a luxury): pigeon, duck, goose, beef, goat and pork perhaps

Honey for sweetening

Drink: beer (very weak), milk, date or grape wine.

The well-off had a very varied diet. There was a good range of bread and cakes, and five or more kinds of beer, with cheerful names like 'the joy-bringer' and 'the heavenly'. Wine-making was sophisticated, and wine and beer were both imported too, together with olive oil and spices. Poor quality wine might be marked 'For taxation', meaning that the Pharaoh's officials were welcome to take it away as tax!

✏ Activities

Children love talking about food, and this is a good way of getting them to think about the differences between Ancient Egyptian life and our own.

▲ Using the list above, make a menu that the poor might eat, and that the rich might eat. How does it compare with today? What is missing that you eat often?

▲ Discuss other differences to do with food – e.g. no processed food (a good or bad thing?), more reliance on local produce (some imports, but only for the rich), problems of storage – how to keep things fresh? Would the hot dry climate help or not? What about flies?

▲ Try to make one or two simple Egyptian recipes for staple things – bread, honey and date cake . This might be something for children to take to try at home.

Egyptian bread

You need: 4 cups of wholemeal flour; a teaspoonful of salt; 2 cups of water.

Mix the flour, water, and salt together. Knead well. Shape into rounds. Leave overnight on a baking tray.

Draw patterns in the loaves and bake for an hour at Gas Mark 4, 180º C, 350º F.

Honey and date sweets

You need: 200 gm dates, cinnamon, chopped walnuts, honey, ground almonds, water.

Mix dates with a little water. Add cinnamon or other spice, and chopped walnuts. Make into shapes, then coat in honey and ground almonds.

FOOD AND DRINK

You are an Egyptian cook. You must get two meals ready. One is for some poor people – farm workers and stone cutters. The other is for some rich and important people – scribes and friends of the Pharaoh.

Remember to make a good healthy meal. Make it as nice as you can.

For Farmworkers and
Stone-cutters

First Course

Main Course

Last Course

To Drink

For Friends of the Pharaoh
and Scribes

First Course

Main Course

Last Course

To Drink

BUYING and SELLING

Background

Because the Pharaoh was absolute ruler and owner of all of Egypt, all trade in theory went through him. It was a centrally-managed economy, a kind of communist state. All large-scale trade was in the hands of the pharaoh . Internally there was no money as such; workers and taxes were paid in kind (stored in warehouses by officials), and exchange of goods was by barter. For example there is a record of tomb cutters being paid: wheat for bread (they made their own), barley for beer, a ration of water, vegetables, dried and fresh fish, ointment, and clothing; with some salt, wine or imported beer for luxuries.

Although there was no money a medium of exchange did develop. Sometimes wheat was used, by weight (easy to measure and needed by everyone, but rather cumbersome to carry about); also copper or silver, by weight again rather than size or shape. A goat might be worth a deben of copper (about 92 g); a deben was divided into 10 kite.

Activities

To Market! is a barter game to show what it may have been like at village level to buy and sell without money. Since men tended to do the heavier work of farming, weaving, stoneworking or whatever, women tended to go to market – a welcome change from hours of grinding grain into flour, an opportunity to meet the neighbours or exchange information, and exercise some choice.

Players have to take their produce to market and exchange it for what they (a) need and (b) would like.

To Market!

Number of players

The game is designed for 5 players. For more or less than this, increase or decrease the number of cards proportionately. There should be 8 cards per player – 4 necessities and 4 luxuries.

Equipment

Copies of the cards on the next two pages. After photocopying, back them with thin card before cutting out. It would be a good idea to colour them, giving each product a different colour, to make them brighter and easier to distinguish. After playing store safely for future use.

For 5 players you should have:

Necessities

Wheat (for bread)	x 5
Barley (for beer)	x 5
Vegetables	x 5
Fish	x 5

Luxuries

Cloth	x 3
Body oil	x 3
Fruit	x 3
Goat	x 3
Pots	x 2
Honey	x 2
Beads	x 2
Eyepaint	x 2 (20 in all)

Rules

1 Shuffle and deal cards to players. Each player should have 8 cards.

2 Look at your cards. This is what you own.

You are going to market to swap what you don't need or want for what you do.

3 By the end of market day you must have at least:

1 Wheat card

1 Barley

1 Vegetables

1 Fish

You may also want some of these:

Pots (for cooking and storing)

Goat (if you like meat or milk)

Fruit

Honey (for sweetening – no sugar)

Oil (to make your body smell nice)

Eyepaint (to look good and keep flies off)

Cloth (for making clothes)

Beads (for necklaces)

Take your produce to market, swap it with your friends, and see what you can get.

Hints

Players may swap one card for one, but you may choose to pay/charge more than one for something you particularly need or want – especially if you can corner the market in something! It is up to the players to decide if this is fair.

Development

▲ You could make this a more elaborate game by dressing up in Egyptian costume to play

▲ You could give particular roles to some players e.g. collect as much wheat as possible for your large family; you love dressing up and want as much body oil, eyepaint and beads as you can get; and so on.

▲ You could vary the game by providing more cards (in good years) or fewer (for bad ones); or perhaps distinguishing between richer and poorer by giving more cards to some than others – if you dare!

Extension

Discuss what a world without money would be like. What would the advantages and disadvantages be? What jobs would no longer exist? How easy or hard would paying for things be? Can you think of a better way of doing things?

WHEAT	BARLEY	VEGETABLES	FISH
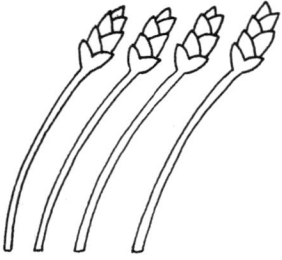	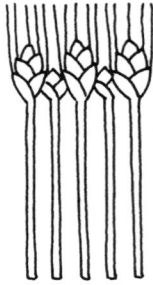		
WHEAT	BARLEY	VEGETABLES	FISH
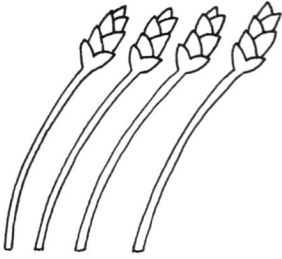	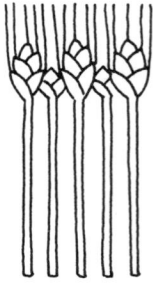		
WHEAT	BARLEY	VEGETABLES	FISH
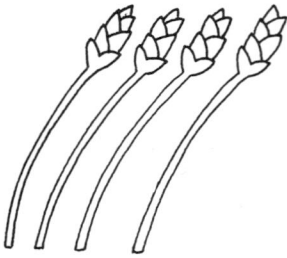	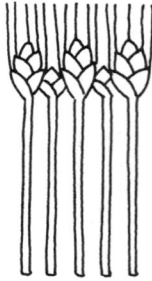	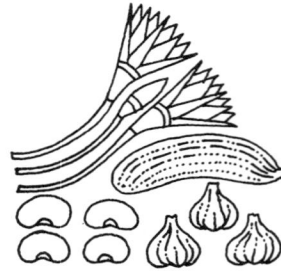	
WHEAT	BARLEY	VEGETABLES	FISH
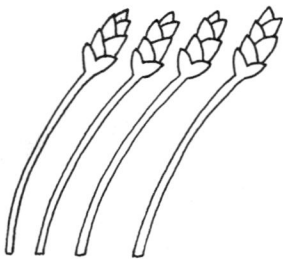	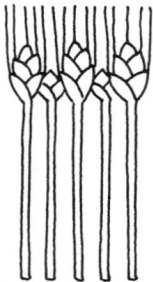		
WHEAT	BARLEY	VEGETABLES	FISH
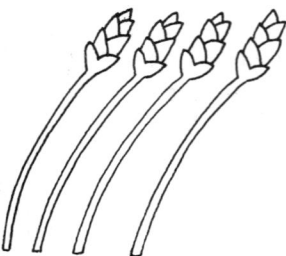	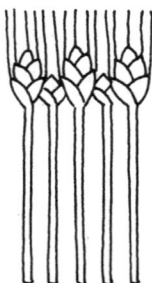		

CLOTH for clothes	CLOTH for clothes	POTS for cooking and storing	POTS for cooking and storing
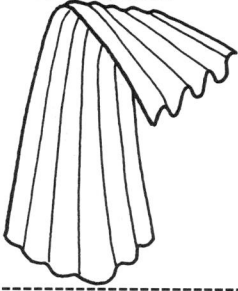	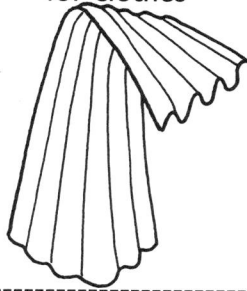		
GOAT	GOAT	BEADS for necklaces	BEADS for necklaces
		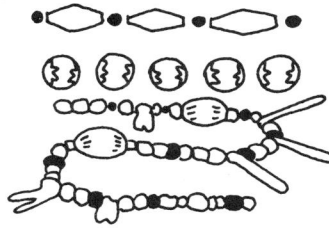	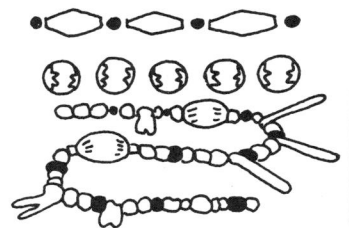
FRUIT	FRUIT	FRUIT	CLOTH for clothes
			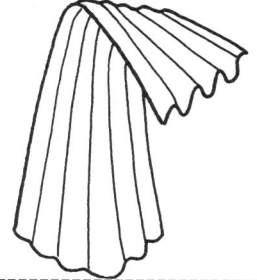
OIL for your body	OIL for your body	OIL for your body	HONEY for sweetening
	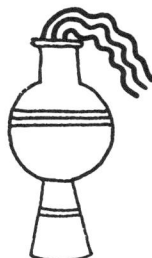		
HONEY for sweetening	CLOTH for clothes	EYEPAINT	EYEPAINT
	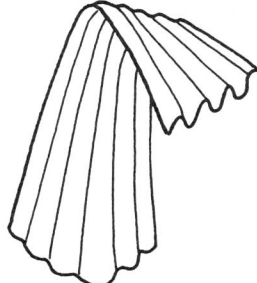	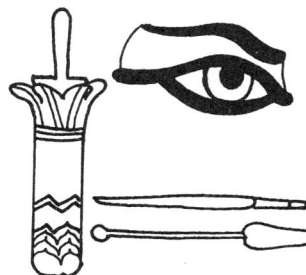	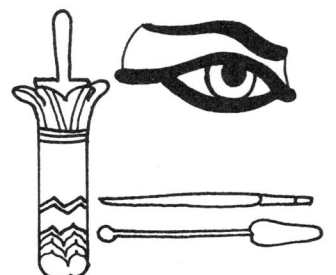

AN EGYPTIAN HOUSE

Background

Egypt was not a city culture, unlike the other ancient civilisations of Mesopotamia and the Indus. In Egypt cities were for religion and temples, pharaohs and government. Most people lived in farms, villages and small towns, along the edge of the Nile flood plain. Sometimes villages on slightly higher ground in the plain would become islands during the inundation.

Houses were made from sun-dried mud bricks. They were rectangular and had a flat roof (where they relaxed and may have slept too). There would be a little yard, an entrance hall, living room, bedroom and kitchen – perhaps for a family of six. The cooking was probably done outside – there would be a quern for grinding flour and an oven for baking bread. Except for some town houses they were one storey only.

Egyptians loved gardens and had one if there was space, with trees, flowers, and a pool for a reservoir.

Even poorer people would put models of simple houses in their dead's tombs for them to inhabit in their afterlife. They are pretty similar to rural Egyptian houses today.

✏ Activities

This model of a small house, and some furniture, were found in the tombs of some Egyptians. They tell us what the houses were like and what furniture they had.

Ask the children to look hard at the pictures and write about them. Say what their houses were like and what furniture they had. How are they different from today?

As usual the evidence for domestic archicture and furnishings comes from tombs. The mud-brick houses themselves have long since crumbled, though there are still remains of the towns built for workers on big building projects.

The aim is to draw a straightforward lesson: what we know about history comes from evidence, and our common sense in interpreting it. The discussion should be open-ended and all responses are useful, however simple they are: the Egyptians lived in houses; they had furniture. More detailed comments could reflect on the style of the house, how the way it was built reflected the climate and way of life of the country (e.g. the balcony on the roof and the small window taking account of the hot weather, the yard for cooking, very little rain, etc), what other furniture they probably had, what it was all used for.

**Attainment target:
AT 3 levels 2,3,4**

AN EGYPTIAN HOUSE

This model of a small house, and some furniture, were found in the tombs of some Egyptians.

They tell us what the houses were like and what furniture they had.

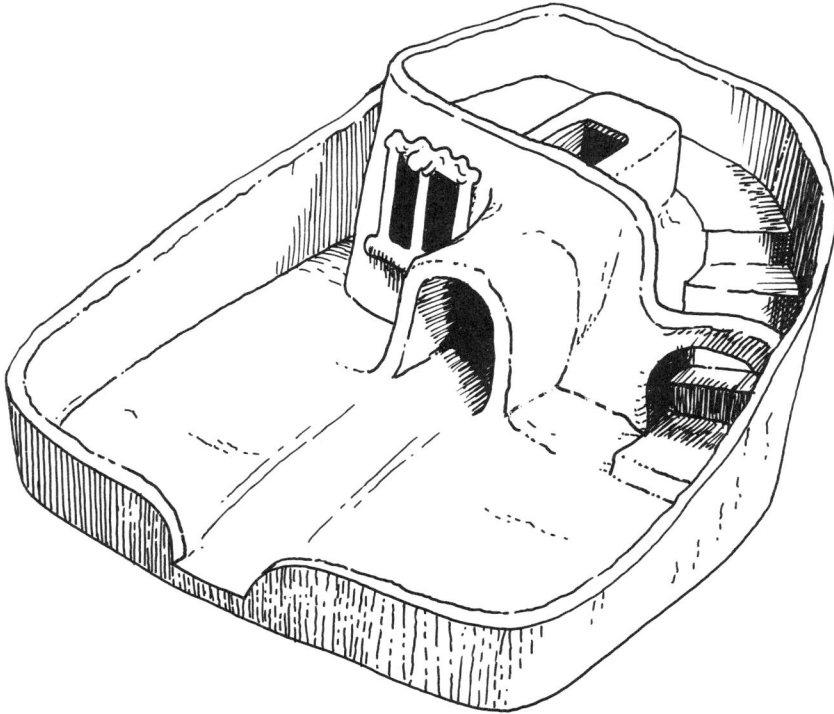

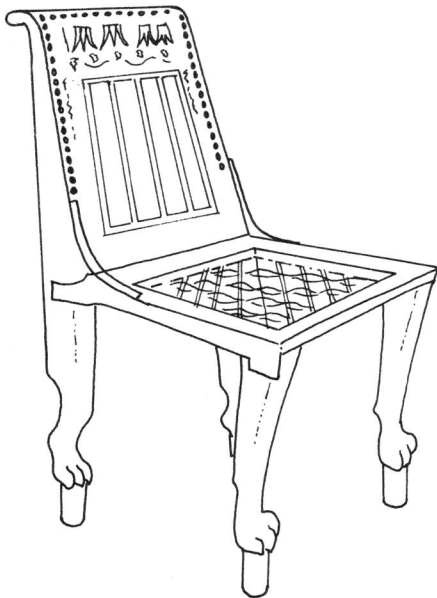

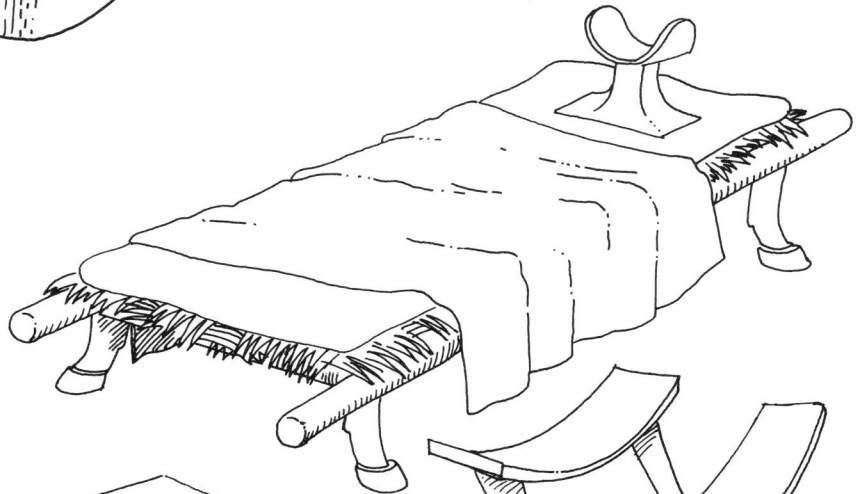

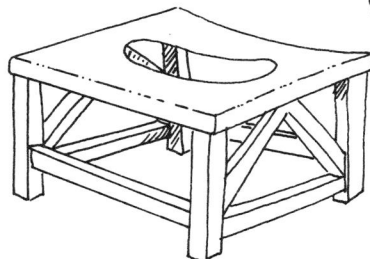

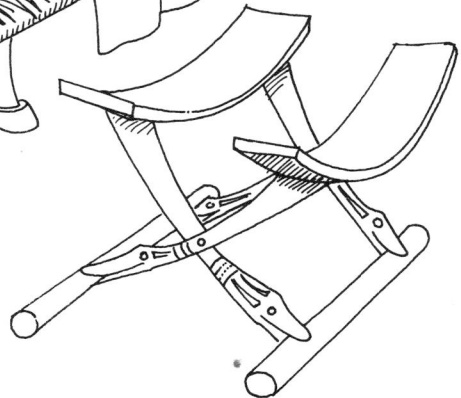

Look hard at the pictures and write about them. Say what their houses were like and what furniture they had. How are they different from today?

DRESS

Background

Egyptians seem to have been dressed simply and elegantly, and mostly in white.

In the Old Kingdom men wore a short loin cloth and women long-sleeved gowns, down to their ankles. Both wore bead necklaces and collars in bright colours. No-one wore underclothes.

There was little change in the Middle Kingdom, though men more often wore tunics on their upper bodies.

In the New Kingdom there was more colour (perhaps allowed by changes in weaving techniques), and more change. Dresses were tighter and finely pleated, shoulders bare, a breast exposed. Children, maids and dancers went naked. Later fashion changed again, back to looser and freer clothes.

Both sexes were very keen on perfume and ointments - the poor just as much as the rich, perhaps because of the dry climate. They oiled their head and hair with animal fat scented with flowers. Women wore rouge and put henna on their nails and the soles of their feet and the palms of their hands. And both men and women wore eye paint, at first medicinally to prevent eye disease and keep off flies, later just to look beautiful. The upper lid was black and the lower green, or both were black.

Richer people also wore loads of jewellery – precious and semi-precious stones, beads, collars of gold. The Pharaoh handed out gold collars to people who had worked well for him – some were weighed down by several.

Finally, wigs were popular with both sexes among the rich. By the New Kingdom they were quite elaborate. The poor could not afford this, and kept their hair quite short. All were clean-shaven, and seemed to have looked down on the hairy-faced Greeks and Asians.

Once again the slowness of change is the most remarkable thing, even when no technological advance or invention is required – compare the developments in fashion in Egypt over 2000 years with European ones over 30 or 40!

✏ Activities

The sheet shows a collection of clothes and ornaments: a man in a loin cloth; a woman in a thin pleated dress; children wearing nothing; wigs with melting balls of perfumed oil on top; beads; rings; and sandals. Discussion could be about comparisons with today – why the Egyptians chose to wear what they did, what has changed, and why; and what has changed very little.

▲ Point out how dress was affected by the hot climate. Do you think they chose their clothes sensibly? What other things affected how they dressed? What do you think about their shoes – are they like anything worn today? Their dress was very simple – one garment each, nothing for children, no underwear; compare that with what we wear. What would be the advantages of simple sorts of clothes, and what drawbacks?

▲ The wigs, beads and jewellery all show how keen they were on ornaments. How does this compare with today – do you think we, or the Egyptians, cared more about looking good? Which of these sorts of ornaments have not changed very much in 4000 years?

**Attainment targets:
AT 1 levels 2,3,4**

DRESSING UP

3 Wigs with balls of nice-smelling oil on top

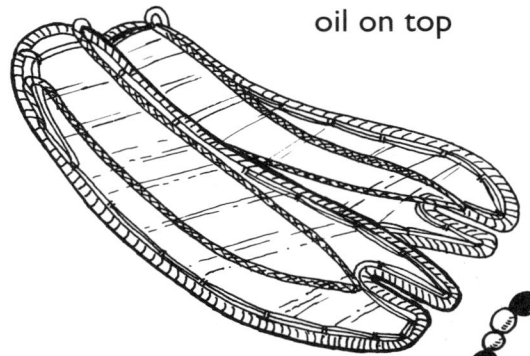

1 Long white dress for women

2 Loin cloth for men

4 Sandals made of rushes

5 No clothes at all for children!

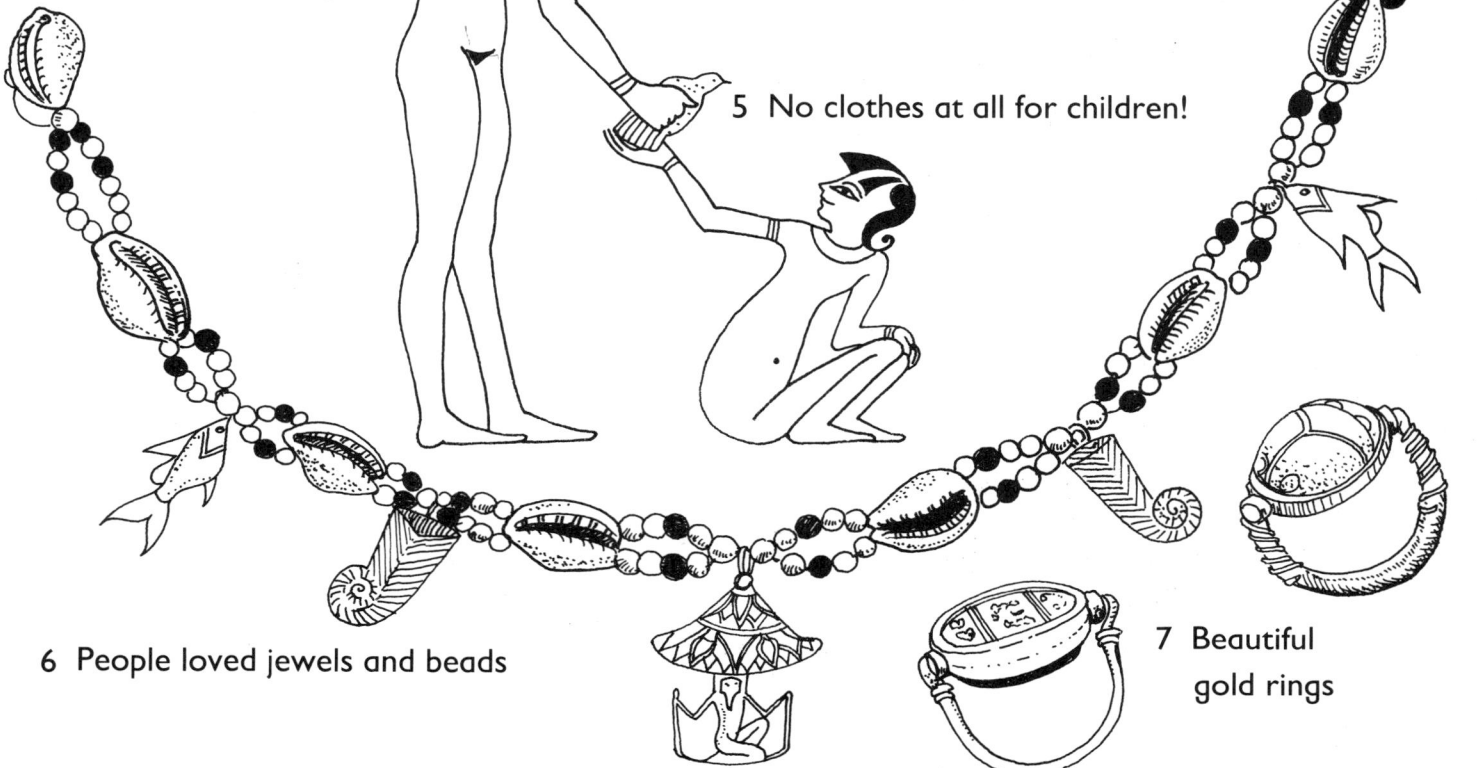

6 People loved jewels and beads

7 Beautiful gold rings

LIFE AT HOME

Background

A picture of everyday life emerges from numerous tomb pictures, stories and artefacts. Compared to many other civilisations, family life seems to have been lived together, with relatively little segregation of men from their families or adults from their children. Wives helped their husbands in the fields, whole families would go hunting or fishing, children and adults would go to the same parties.

As everywhere until recently, families were large and people died young - an adult might expect to live to perhaps 40, but huge numbers must have died in childbirth, infancy and childhood. Because of the high mortality rate, remarriage must have been common.

Women must have spent many hours each day grinding flour, bent on their knees over stones or boards (as usual Egypt was slow to take advantage of labour-saving developments such as a circular mill). Women went to market, especially if there was heavier work to be done at home; but they did not go out to work on their own - with a very few exceptions, the only careers open to them were priestess, dancer, temple concubine or prostitute.

They were in a better position than women in many other societies in marriage, however. Marriage was a private contract between the two partners (some marriages were arranged) and divorce the same, which meant that either could end the marriage. Women owned property and could keep it after marriage, not something that happened in Europe much before the 20th century. They could claim maintenance and generally had equal legal rights with their husbands. Polygamy was not illegal but does not seem to have been practised, except by pharaohs.

Only a few children learned to read and write, and almost no girls. Boys who went to school did so at about the age of five, and learned by copying sentences in praise of scribes and denigrating other professions onto boards covered with gesso (plaster). They were beaten if they were slow to learn. There were senior schools called Houses of Life, attached to temples, where advanced study took place in medicine, astronomy, mathematics, science and law. Otherwise adult life started with marriage at about 12 and work helping parents or elsewhere. Girls stayed at home in childhood and helped in the house.

✐ Activities

On the page is a list of ways in which life would have been different for Egyptian children, compared to life today. By deciding which aspects were better, and which worse, children can try to get an idea of what growing up in Ancient Egypt would have been like, and which aspects of life have changed most and which least.

**Attainment targets:
AT1 levels 2,3,4**

GROWING UP IN ANCIENT EGYPT

What was it like to be a child in Ancient Egypt? Here is a list of ways in which it was different from your life today.

Make two lists for yourself. Write in one list the things which you think were better than now. Write in the other list the things which were worse.

Better than now	Worse than now

SCHOOL

1 Very hard learning to read and write
2 Beaten if slow to learn
3 Only a few boys went to school
4 Girls didn't go to school
5 Left school at the age of 12

HOME

1 Food mostly the same all the time (bread, beer, vegetables, fish)
2 Simple wooden toys and games
3 Lots of brothers and sisters
4 Simple clothes – just a white tunic
5 Cat, dog or monkey for pet
6 Outside most of the time
7 Help your parents with work in fields
8 Hunting and fishing in the river
9 A canoe for each family
10 Married at about 12 – 14
11 No pills for headaches or illness
12 Died quite young

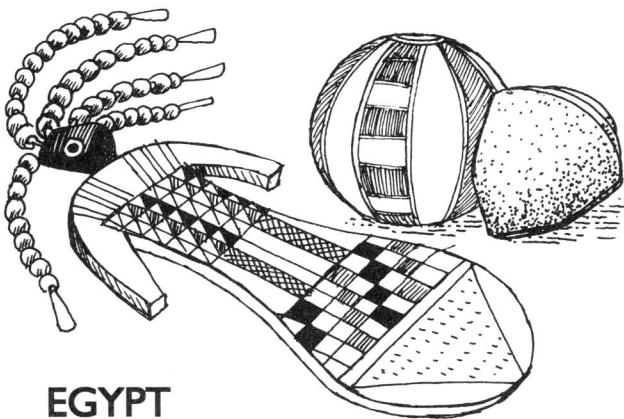

EGYPT

1 Hot, fine weather, very little rain
2 Each week 10 days long (one or two days off)
3 4 months of flood each year – no work if you are lucky
4 No roads or traffic – travel up and down the river
5 Crocodiles in the river

Would you rather have lived now or then?

ANIMALS

Background

Egyptians had a close relationship with animals, in several different ways.

They loved keeping pets, of which the most common were cats, dogs and monkeys.

They used animals of course in farming – oxen and donkeys for hauling, goats, pigs and sheep. Sheep were sometimes used for treading in grain after it had been sown. There was a fat-tailed sheep whose tail was so large and heavy that it was supported on a little trolley. Even the very poor would have a goat. There were rules against eating pork, but these may not always have been observed. The horse did not arrive from Asia until c.1600 BC.

The richer people loved hunting, for lion, hippopotamus, antelope, gazelle. The first two of these were hunted almost to extinction. Some of it was more fencing off and killing than hunting. They speared water-fowl in the marshes from their canoes and netted migrant birds. And they fished.

Some animals had strong religious connections. Gods were worshipped in the form of animals in the Old Kingdom and Late Period, and as human bodies with animal heads in the Middle and New Kingdoms. Some animals were sacred to particular gods - baboons to Thoth, bulls to Ptah, cats to Bastet, rams and crocodiles. Cats sacred to Bastet lived in the temple and were mummified or buried in large cat cemeteries when they died. Other animals were also mummified.

✏ Activities

On the page are some pieces of first-hand evidence – all pictures from tombs showing animals in different situations. You could ask the children about each picture: first, what does it show? Second, what does it tell us about animals in Egypt? There is space under each picture to write something. They may also be coloured and cut out for project books.

The pictures show:

1 Pet cat with a bone (?) under her mistress's chair. (This picture tells us that Egyptians had pet cats which were allowed indoors – also something about dress and furniture.)

2 Baboons in a fig tree. (Are these pet baboons, or are they wild? Playing, or pests? It has been suggested that they were trained to pick fruit.)

3 A hippopotamus hunt. (Tells us about implements used for hunt, that they did hunt hippos, that there *were* hippos in the Nile – there are no hippos or crocodiles in Egypt now; what about the hippo attacking the crocodile?)

4 Man with hare, antelope(?), plate of eggs. (They hunted hares and collected eggs (ostrich I think) for delicacies. What is the antelope doing? The picture suggests that it is tamed, but perhaps has been captured?)

5 Man with dogs. (They had dogs for pets, and used them for hunting? Note collars and leashes, quite like today.)

Extension

How useful are these pictures as historical sources? What other evidence would you like to find which would help you to be sure about Egyptians and animals?

Attainment targets:
AT 2 level 4; AT 3 levels 1-5.

ANIMALS IN EGYPT

1 . . . .
. . . .

2 . . . .
. . . .

3 . . . .
. . . .

4 . . . .
. . . .

5 . . . .
. . . .

☥ ☥ THE PHARAOHS ☥ ☥

Background

The Pharaoh (the name, meaning 'Great House', did not come into use until the New Kingdom) was absolute ruler in every respect. He held all power and owned all property. He was high priest, chief justice, head of administration, field marshal, and god incarnate. The Egyptians even believed that it was his power that made the Nile flood.

The Pharaoh assumed all these powers, including the godship, on his coronation. He was crowned with the Double Crown, the White Crown of Upper Egypt and the Red Crown of Lower Egypt. He wore a bull's tail to symbolise his strength and a false beard to show his godship.

His wife was called the Great Royal Wife (he had several subsidiary wives too, probably, and a harem). The succession to the throne was through the female line, which meant that the man who married the Pharaoh's daughter would become Crown Prince and the next Pharaoh. Often the girl's brother would marry her, to keep the crown in the family; if not, usually a lesser relation. Some pharaohs even married their daughters themselves, probably to maximise the chances of a satisfactory succession. These generations of incest do not appear to have done the many dynasties of pharaohs any harm.

The Pharaoh became several gods, at different times. Early on he was the incarnation of the sky god Horus. Later on his godship was less overpowering and he was recognised as the son of the sun god Re. When he died he became the god Osiris.

The Pharaoh had to be a good soldier, huntsman and sportsman as well as everything else. Beneath him was an enormous bureaucracy headed by the chief vizier, who was in charge of irrigation, taxation, the cattle census, royal expeditions, building projects, justice, all appointments, and so on. He was usually a relation of the Pharaoh, as were many of the officials.

The Pharaoh was surrounded by a court of courtiers, including a spokesman, scribe, holder of the sunshade, and fanbearers.

Only a few women are known to have been pharaoh in their own right. The longest ruling pharaoh was Pepi II, who was on the throne for 94 years – probably a record for any monarch anywhere.

✏ Activities

This activity involves chronological ordering, with some mathematics. You need to get across the idea that dates BC went backwards i.e. that 400 came after 500, and not before. Children may colour the portraits and stick them in their time lines.

Extension questions:

1 Who ruled the longest and shortest? How do they compare to our Queen?

2 How do their powers compare to modern rulers and governments?

3 Which pharaohs look good/nice, and which bad/nasty? Why do you think so?

4 These pictures come from statues set up by the pharaohs themselves? Do you think they really looked liked this, or did they try to make themselves look better than they really were?

5 These pharaohs cover an enormous time span – more than 2500 years from the first to the last. It is a shorter time from Cleopatra to today than from Djoser to Cleopatra. Can you compare that time (span to British history or rulers?

Attainment targets:
AT 1 levels 1,2

☥ ☥ SOME PHARAOHS ☥ ☥

There were hundreds of Pharaohs in Egyptian history. Here are six of them. Work out how long each of them ruled. Colour and cut them out and put them in order, from the earliest to the last.

I am Cleopatra.
I ruled from 51 to 30 BC.
I was the last Pharaoh.
I loved Julius Ceasar.
In the end I killed myself.
I ruled for . . . . years.

I am Hatshepsut.
I ruled from 1473 to 1458 BC.
I was a queen, a female
pharaoh.
I made Egypt peaceful and rich.
I ruled for . . . . years.

I am Ramesses II.
I ruled from 1290 to 1224 BC.
I fought many battles and built
huge temples and statues of
myself.
I ruled for . . . . years.

I am Senwosret III..
I ruled from 1878 to 1841 BC.
I conquered Nubia, the land
to the south.
I ruled for . . . . . . years.

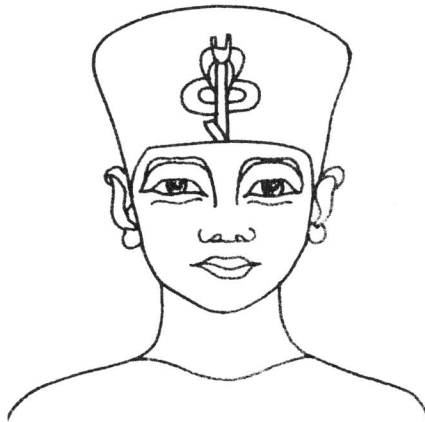

I am Tutankhamun.
I ruled from 1333 to 1323 BC.
I became king when I was
only 8 years old.
I ruled for . . . . . . years.

I am Djoser.
I ruled from 2630 to 2611 BC.
I The first pyramid was built
for me.
I ruled for . . . . . . years.

TUTANKHAMUN

Background

Tutankhamun's tomb is the only pharaoh's tomb to have been discovered that is more or less intact; so it is the only direct knowledge we have of a pharaoh's funeral and the things that were considered important enough to him to put in his tomb.

Tutankhamun, a king of the 18th Dynasty, reigned probably c.1333-1323 BC. He was about 18 when he died (we know this from analysis of his bones), possibly from a head injury. His proper tomb was not ready when he died, so he was hastily buried in a smaller tomb which was being got ready for his powerful vizier Ay. So everything was crammed in to a much smaller space than would have been normal.

Tutankhamun's tomb was discovered by Howard Carter in 1922. It had been robbed, but only smaller items had been taken. The remaining treasures, more than 2000 objects, were piled together in the four rooms of the tomb. There were three coffins, the third innermost one made of solid gold weighing 1140 kg. There were masses of other gold things, also precious stones and alabaster.

Tutankhamun's reign followed that of the controversial Akhenaten and his wife Nefertiti, who had abolished worship of all gods except Aten (represented by the sun's disc) and moved the capital from Thebes north to a new site (now El-Amarna). Tutankhamun moved the capital back to Thebes and restored the chief state god Amun-Re. After his death his wife Ankhesenamun wrote to the Hittite king asking him to send a prince to marry her and become pharaoh – she probably wanted to avoid being made to marry the vizier Ay! But she may have married him, because the aging Ay became the next pharaoh.

Activities

The children should paste the photocopied sheet onto thin card before colouring and cutting out. The mask is gold and blue, with some red – refer to one of the numerous colour photographs as a guide for the colouring.

The original mask is made of solid gold. On its forehead are the cobra of Edjo, the goddess of Lower Egypt, and the vulture of Nekhbet, the goddess of Upper Egypt. The beard is the symbol of godship.

THE MASK OF TUTANKHAMUN

Background

Pyramids date from about 2600 BC. Kings used to be buried in mastabas, long low rectangular structures which looked a bit like benches, which is what 'mastaba' means. The inventor of pyramids was probably Imhotep, the chief official of the pharaoh Djoser. Imhotep had the idea of a building which looked like a number of mastabas built on top of each other, gradually getting smaller as they went higher. This was the Step Pyramid, the first built in Egypt. It was 125 x 110 m in area and 60 m high.

Shortly after this the first true pyramids were built. The two great pyramids at Giza are the largest buildings ever constructed by humans, the Great Pyramid being about 230 m square and 146 m high. It is made of 2,300,000 blocks of stone weighing more than two tons each, and took 23 years to build. Napoleon calculated that its stones would make a wall three metres high round the borders of France!

The sheer effort of building something on this scale, especially as it was not directly connected to material life, is astonishing, and shows how well the Old Kingdom must have been organised. There was perhaps a regular workforce of 4,000 or so, swollen to 50,000 when villagers were summoned when agricultural work was not being done. There were no pulleys, scaffolding or even wheels to help them – the heavy stone blocks were hauled up earth ramps on sleds by human muscle.

A royal pyramid complex consisted of the pyramid itself with a mortuary temple next to it, where the cult of the king could be pursued, smaller temples for queens, all surrounded by a wall, and a causeway leading to the valley temple beside the river. The Egyptians had elegant and elaborate names for the pyramids, such as 'The Pyramid Which is the Place of Sunrise and Sunset' (The Great Pyramid) and 'The Shining and Beautiful Pyramid'.

After the end of the Old Kingdom (c.2100 BC) pyramids were much smaller. The cost and effort of building them was just too great, they were running out of suitable land, and they attracted grave robbers - all the old pyramids were eventually robbed, even though the builders tried to make the corridors inside as complicated as possible. During the Middle Kingdom, about 1700 BC, they stopped building them altogether.

Imhotep was the first human genius whose name we know. As well as architecture he practised sculpture and medicine, and was later worshipped as a god of healing.

✏ Activities

1 Drawings of Pyramids

Resources for a project folder. Children could arrow or number and name, with explanations:

for Step Pyramid
1 pyramid; 2 surrounding wall; 3 entrance; 4 festival buildings.

and for True Pyramid
1 pyramid; 2 wall; 3 queen's pyramid; 4 mortuary temple; 5 causeway; 6 valley temple.

They could also add a line or two of their own about each pyramid.

2 Making models of pyramids

Glue a sheet of card (postcard thickness) to the back of the page, and colour the pyramid before cutting out (though they were originally a brilliant white). Give an idea of the colossal scale of the Great Pyramid, and the little queen pyramids next to it. The huge scale of the Great Pyramid makes it necessary to make 4 copies of this sheet!

3 For discussion

Why did they build pyramids, on such a huge scale and cost, when ordinary tombs might have done just as well? What was in it for them?

Why pyramids especially – why that shape? (Possibly chosen because they pointed at the Sun-God?). How did they manage to build them? – discuss problems of lifting huge weights without wheels or pulleys. Can you think of ways of getting the blocks up the steep slopes (ramps, sleds, lifting using a balance?). Can you work out the total weight of a pyramid? How did they manage to be so accurate in their calculations of the slope, when they did not have protractors or anything to measure angles?

Attainment targets: AT 1 levels 2,3,4

☼ TWO KINDS OF PYRAMID ☼

1 Step Pyramid

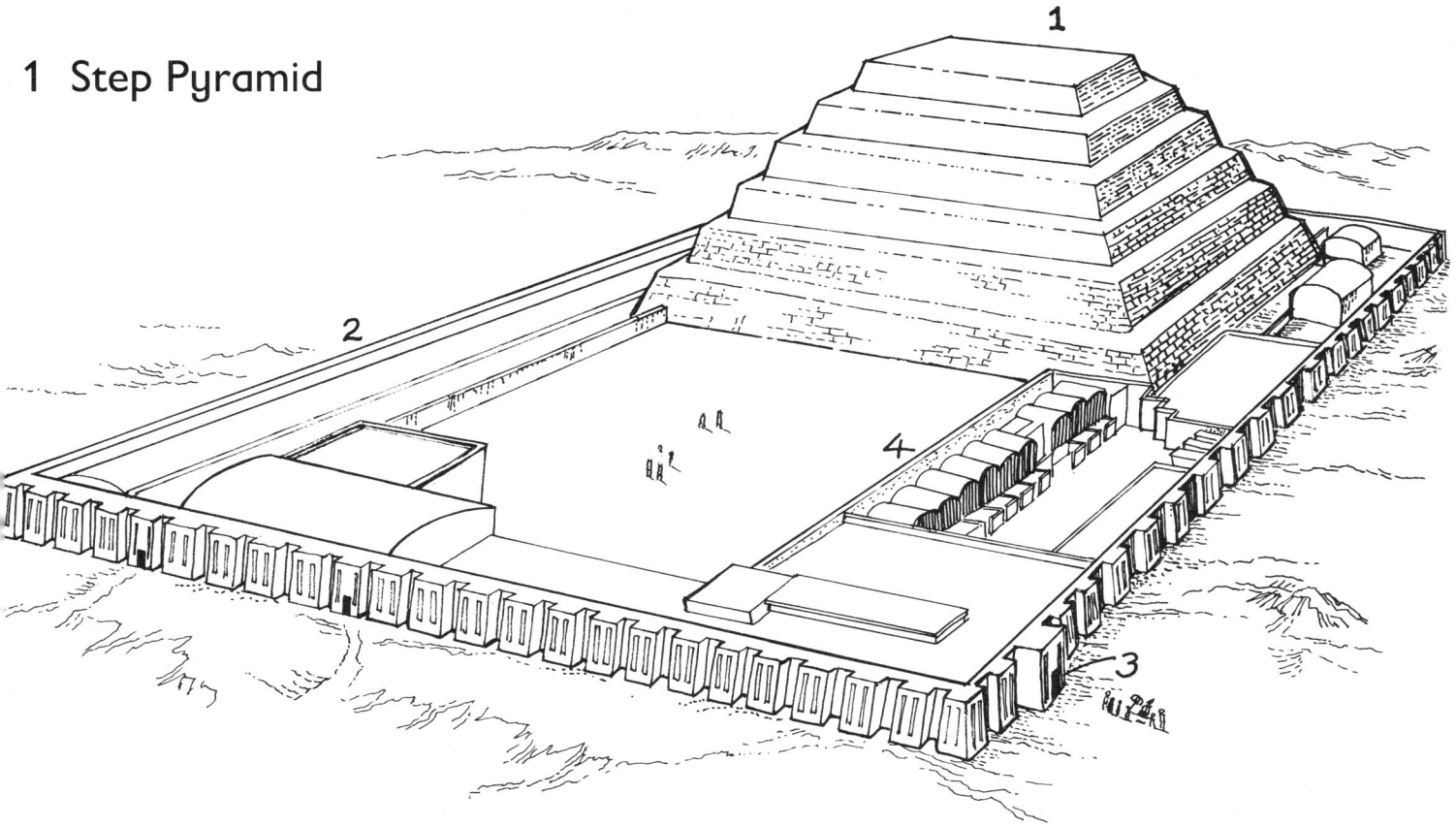

2 True Pyramid

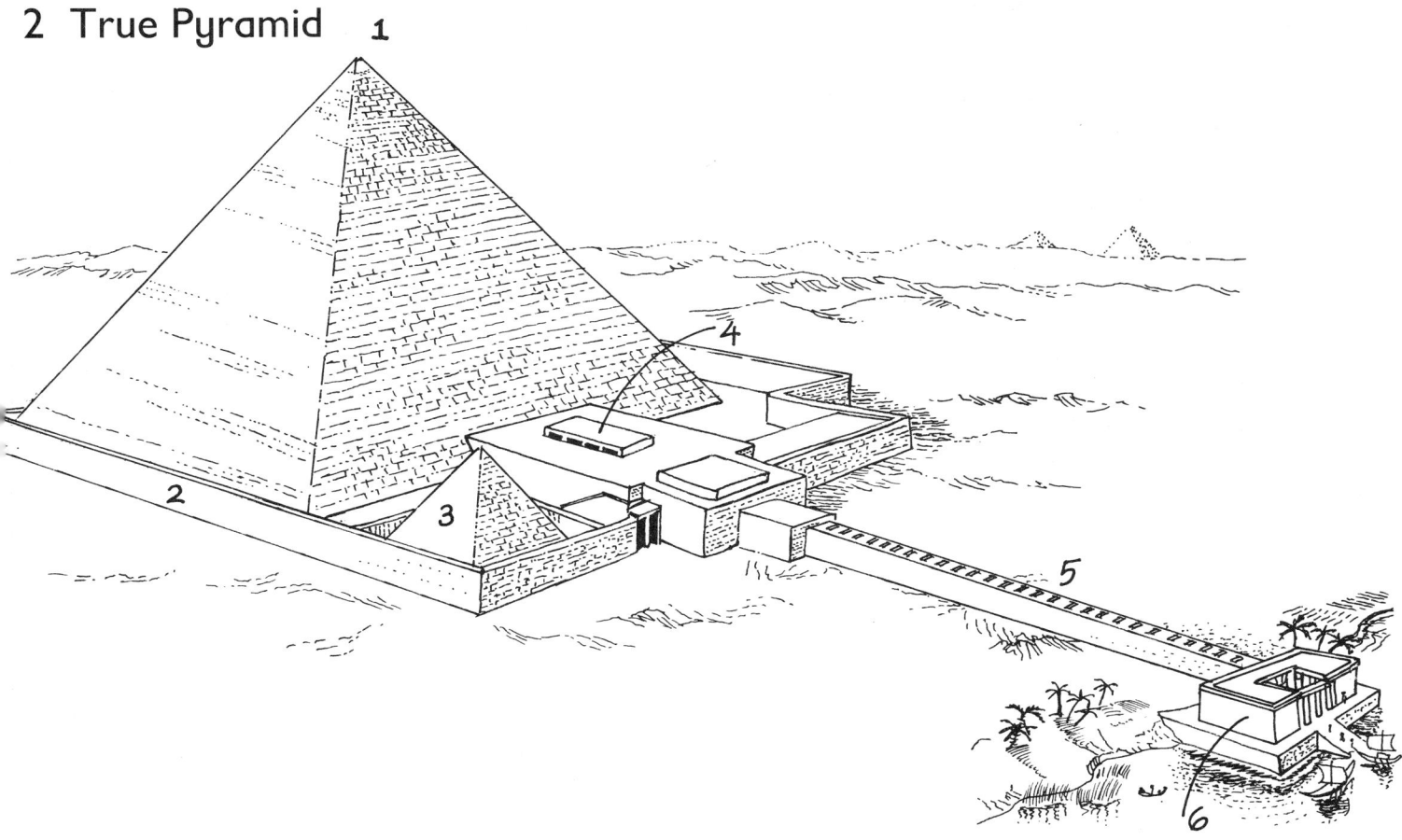

bottom

Scale: 1mm = 1 metre

You need 4 copies of this sheet, to make the 4 sides of the Great Pyramid. Stick a thin piece of card to the back of your sheet and colour your pyramid before cutting it out.

Cut along lines.
Fold along dotted lines.
Glue tabs and fold under.

After finishing it cut a piece of card 230mm square to stick underneath your pyramid.

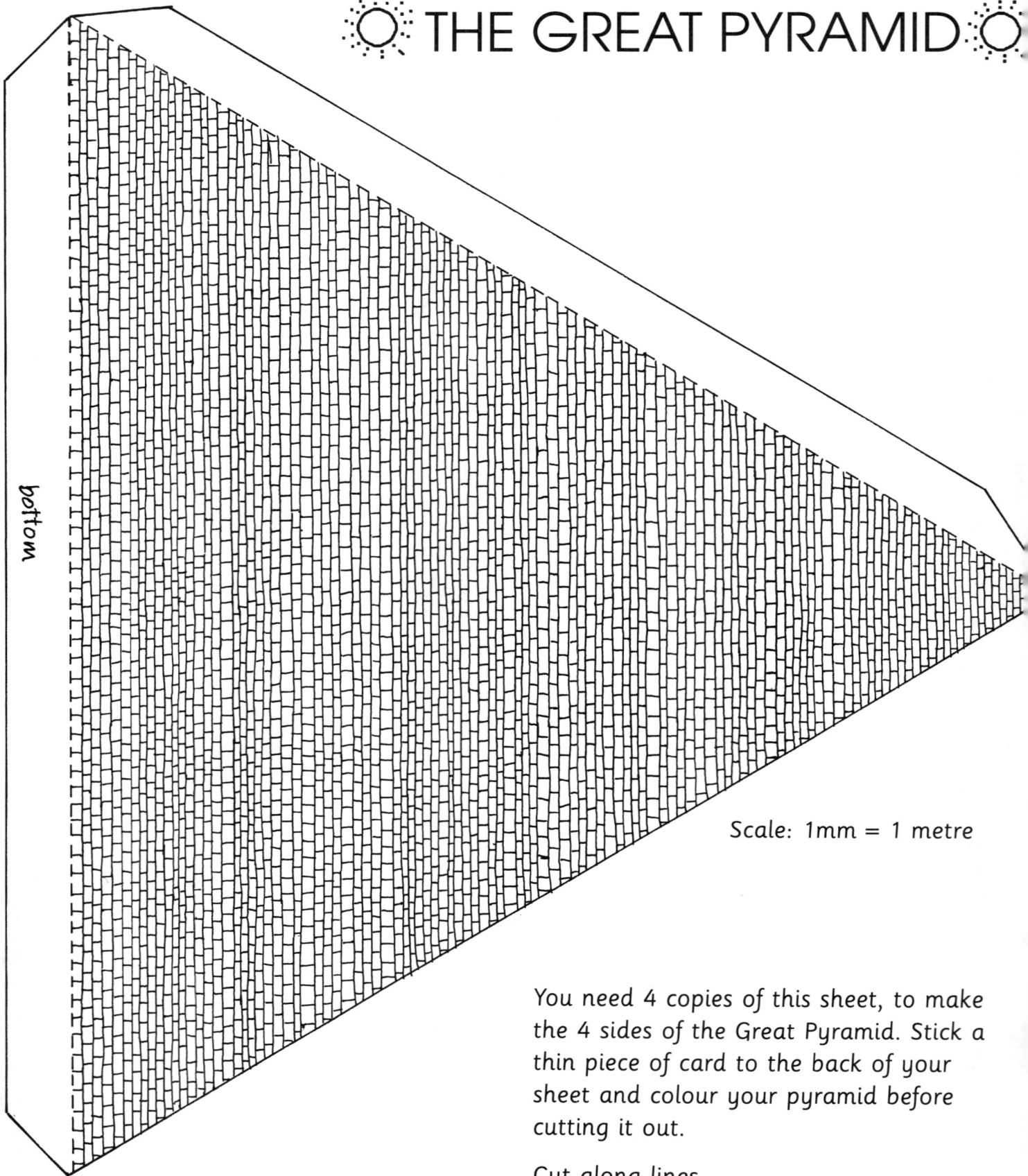

© History Timelines: Ancient Egypt – J F Nash/Simon & Schuster Education 1993

☼ SMALL PYRAMID ☼

☼ QUEEN PYRAMID ☼

Stick a thin piece of card to the back of your sheet and colour your pyramids before cutting them out.

Cut along lines.
Fold along dotted lines.
Glue tabs and fold under.

After finishing them cut a piece of card to stick underneath your pyramids.

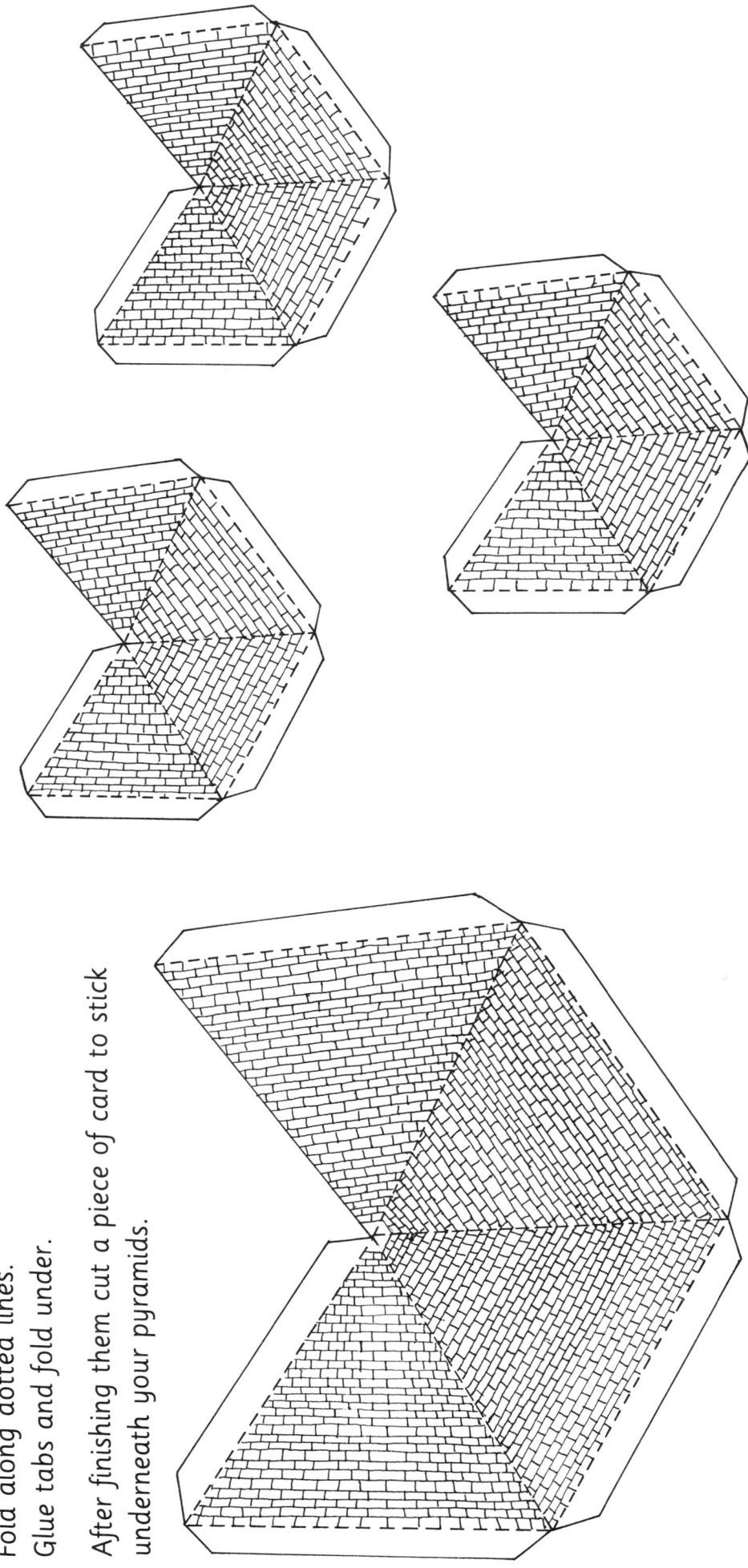

Scale: 1mm = 1metre

DEATH AND BURIAL

Background

The Egyptians were not obsessed by death, although it may appear so. It is partly that almost everything we know about Egyptian life comes from things and pictures found in their tombs; and partly that the Egyptians seem to have loved life so much that their aim in the afterlife was to enjoy as near to this life as possible, with some improvements (e.g. less work).

For a successful afterlife a person needed his name, his body, food and drink, and the various conveniences of this life (some tombs were even equipped with lavatories). The texts and pictures left in the tomb recorded and continued his name. The body was preserved as a mummy. Food and drink was provided by the tomb servants, and by magic when the tomb servants gave up.

In his afterlife a person had a Ka, a Ba, and an Akh – all aspects of what we would call a soul or self. The Ka was the spiritual essence or self of a person, and the tomb was its home. It was the Ka which needed the food and drink, the things left in the tomb, and so on. The Ba was the soul: represented as a human-headed bird, it left the tomb in the day to revisit the world, and returned to the Ka in the tomb at night. The Akh was the soul in the afterlife, which was seen at different times as a field of rushes, or the stars.

This is an oversimplified description; beliefs changed over time, and some were contradictory. In the Old Kingdom ordinary people did not have afterlives at all; they were reserved for royalty. But the later cult of Osiris was open to all. The dead person was tested by 42 assessor gods, denying a sin to each one, with scales balancing his heart (Intelligence) against a feather (Truth). When he passed this test the dead person was declared 'true of voice' and led to Osiris to begin his afterlife.

The ritual of burial was long and detailed. The whole process took 70 days. First the brain was removed, by hooks through the nose, and the other organs except the heart. The corpse was then drained of fluid and packed in a natural chemical called nitron, which dried the body out, for about six weeks. They then stuffed, anointed, washed and perfumed it, and finally wrapped it tightly in a number of different bandages to restore its human form. This was all done while prayers were said, by men sometimes wearing dogs' head masks, representing Anubis, the god of burial. The mummy was then enclosed in a painted man-shaped coffin, in turn inside one or two further coffins, and stored, perhaps standing up, in the burial chamber.

At the end was the ceremony of the 'opening of the mouth', which was intended to restore to the deceased the power to eat, speak, move about, and so on. The lungs, liver, intestine and stomach were stored in four jars called Canopic jars, watched over by four gods and four goddesses. This was the expensive way, and the Greek historian Herodotus notes that it depended on how rich you were. For the poorer classes, he says, 'They just wash out the inside with a solvent, then pickle it for seventy days and return it to the relatives.'

44

DEATH AND BURIAL

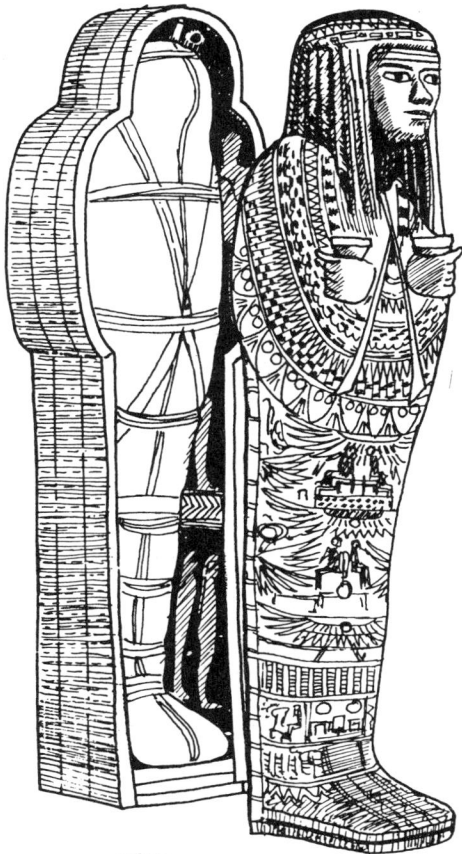

This is a mummy. It . . .

This is Anubis. He . . .

This is a shabti. It . . .

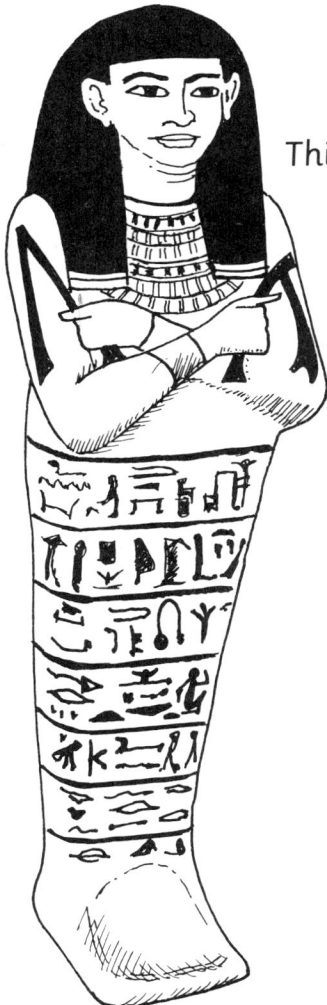

This food and drink is for . . .

GODS AND GODDESSES

Background

There were many local gods in ancient Egypt, and most of the important national gods came originally from one region. Some gods were humble household ones and some were all-powerful national gods. They rose and fell in importance during the 3000 years of history.

The Egyptians did not worship animals but they did worship their gods in the forms of animals (though not all of them), and worshippers made offerings to gods in the form of real and model animals.

There are a number of creation myths. The most important one says that the original god of creation was Atum or Atum-Re, who rose on a hill out of a watery chaos. Atum gave birth to Shu (air) and Tefnut (moisture), who in turn gave birth to Geb (earth) and Nut (sky). Their children were Osiris and his sister/wife Isis, and Seth and Nephys. The myth goes that Osiris was murdered and torn to pieces by his jealous brother Seth, but was put together by Isis just enough to conceive their son Horus, who avenged Osiris in a long battle against Seth. Horus was identified with Life, and all living kings; Osiris with the underworld and all dead kings.

Here is a short list of some of the gods:

Amun   the chief god of Thebes, identified with Re; shown as a man

Anubis   necropolis god; patron of embalmers; shown as jackal

Aten   god of the sun-disc

Bastet   cat goddess

Geb   the Earth god, husband of Nut; shown as a man

Hapy   god of the Nile in flood; shown as a man with breasts and papyrus on his head

Hathor   cow goddess; goddess of love, birth, death; identified by Greeks with Aphrodite

Horus   identified with the king in his lifetime; the son and avenger of Osiris; shown with a falcon for a head

Isis   holy mother, wife of Osiris and mother of Horus; one of the four protector-goddesses guarding coffins and Canopic jars

Khepri   the scarab beetle god; identified with Re as a creator

Nut   the sky-goddess, wife of Geb; shown with her naked body curved to form the arch of heaven

Osiris   the god of the underworld; the dead king; god of flooding and vegetation; shown as mummified king

Ptah   creator god of Memphis; patron of craftsmen

Re   sun god of Heliopolis; supreme judge; linked to Amun and Atum; falcon-headed

Seth   brother and murderer of Osiris; god of storms and violence; identified with different animals, including pig and hippopotamus

Shu   god of air; shown as man separating sky from earth

Thoth   the scribe of the gods, inventor of writing; ibis head

Activities

Figures to colour and cut out or paste into project books. The names of the gods should be written onto the tabs. If cutting out, back the sheet first with thin card.

Ask the children to add something in their own words about each god.

The gods on the page are:

Bastet – cat – goddess of war

Horus – hawk – god of sky

Anubis – jackal – god of mummies

Thoth – ibis(bird) – god of writing and counting

Isis – woman – goddess of magic

Osiris – man – ruler of the dead

For extension

Choose one god and write a prayer to him or her, for something you need, or want to avoid.

GODS AND GODDESSES

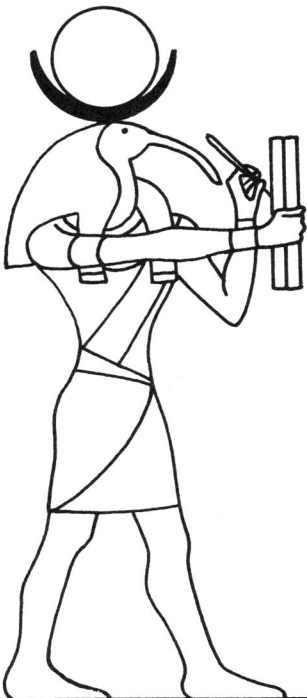

❈❈❈TEMPLES AND PRIESTS❈❈❈

Background

After the great days of pyramid building were over, pharaohs built colossal temples all over the country, dedicated to Amun-Re and the other gods. There were enormous numbers of priests to serve them, and to perform other duties for the dead, and large amounts of land were given to temples to support them with food, manpower and so on. In time the temples and priests became powers themselves almost as great as the pharaoh, and for a time at the end of the New Kingdom (c.1000 BC) the priests of Thebes ruled the southern half of Egypt directly.

The temples were the place where the king could communicate with the gods, and the priest's job was to stand in for the pharaoh in the daily temple ceremony. This took place each day, and went roughly as follows:

▲ dawn procession

▲ ritual purification and dressing of the priest

▲ lighting a fire and incense

▲ opening the shrine containing the statue of the god

▲ incense, hymns, offering honey or the figure of the goddess Maat (representing order in the land)

▲ stripping, purifying and reclothing the figure of the god/offering food in a ritual feast

▲ closing the doors and purifying the sanctuary.

From outside the temples looked like fortresses, surrounded by a high sacred wall. The entrance was between huge towers into a graceful outer courtyard, with colonnades and pillars. Beyond this was the hall, with various rooms off, and then the sanctuary where the daily ritual took place.

Priestesses played a subsidiary role but an important one – singing, dancing and mourning. It was said of a god :'singing, dancing and incense are his food'.

✏ Activities

The drawings opposite are of

1 a temple

2 a priest

3 a priestess

Ask the children to put a title and a brief explanation against each picture.

You could also use these pictures as the basis for creative writing on 'A Day in My Life', by a priest.

**Attainment targets:
AT 1 levels 2-4**

⧓⧓ TEMPLES AND PRIESTS ⧓⧓

1 Temple

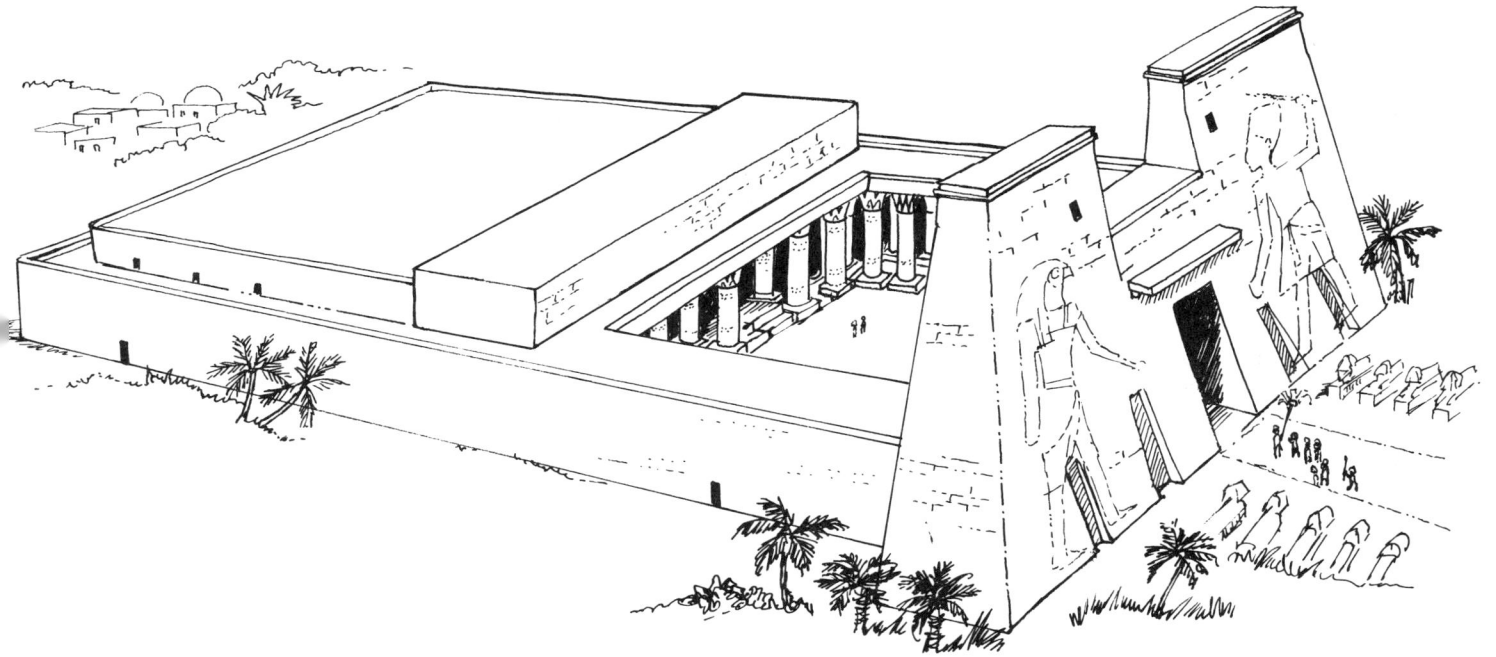

2 Priest

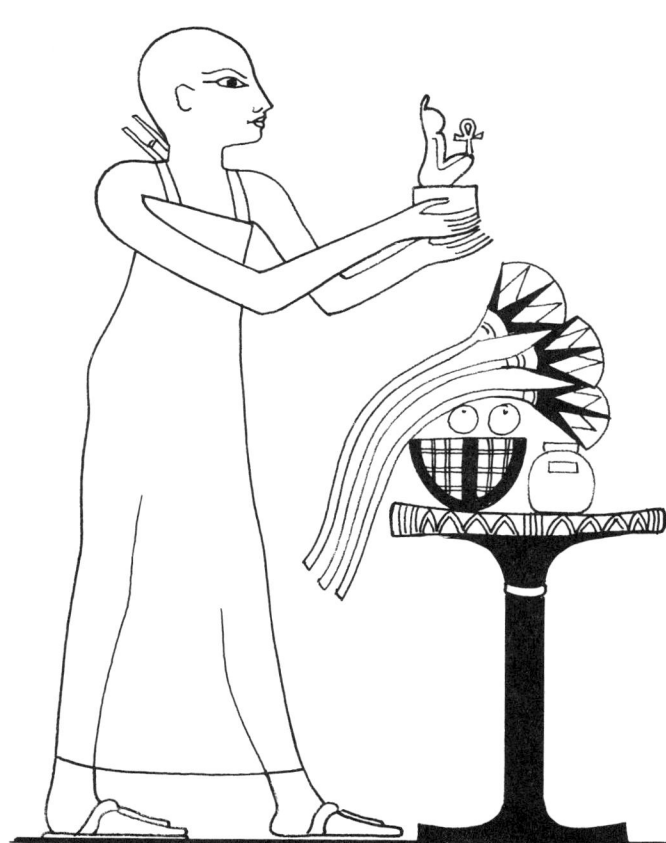

3 Priestess

WRITING

Background

From c.3100 BC to 300 AD the Egyptians used the hieroglyphic script. Writing had already been invented, by the Sumerians, but the Egyptians seem to have developed their own system from scratch.

There were more than 700 different signs, so it is not surprising that learning to read and write was an arduous process, that only a very small minority learned at all, and that the profession of scribe was influential and prestigious.

There were two kinds of hieroglyphic sign: phonograms, which were basically consonants representing one, two or three letters of our own alphabet; and ideograms, which presented the pictorial meaning of a word – e.g. a sun, or a figure of a man or woman after a name. They did not use vowels, so it is practically impossible to work out how words were pronounced.

There were two other kinds of script: hieratic, which was a kind of cursive hieroglyphic, for writing fast, which became a system of writing of its own after a while; and demotic, another cursive style which was invented very late in ancient Egypt's history. Scribes used hieratic for everyday writing, business and so on, and hieroglyphic for more formal inscriptions, monuments and religious affairs. Hieroglyphs could be written left to right, right to left, or vertically, but hieratic came to be written always right to left.

As everyone knows the Egyptians invented papyrus as the forerunner of paper. They took the long papyrus reed stems, peeled off the outer skin, cut the inside into strips lengthwise, and laid the strips together; then laid a second layer across the first at right angles and pressed or beat them together, and then polished the end-product into a smooth writing surface. Schoolboys used wooden boards painted with plaster, with holes in them for hanging up.

Very few Egyptian words have come down to us. The Greeks invented the name for Egypt, and for pyramid. A few words which are originally Egyptian are: Susan, from *shoshen*, a lotus-flower; ebony, hard black wood; gum, gum from the acacia tree; sack, a receptacle, from *sok*, to collect; ibis, the stork-like bird; oasis.

Activities

This is a very simple introduction to the idea of hieroglyphics. The words to work out are of course English words, not Egyptian ones, which would have led to too many complications. The points to draw out are

▲ The skill and time it took to draw the letters , and the time it must have taken to learn 700 of them – this partly explains why few learned to write and why it was a highly prized skill

▲ How modern writing is much faster and more flexible in comparison, and how nearly everybody now can write. Why did the Egyptians stick to such a cumbersome system? (Very slow to change compared to the modern world? Scribes wanting to protect their jobs?)

▲ Are they any other picture-writing systems anywhere in the world that people know of (Chinese?)?

EGYPTIAN WRITING

The Egyptians used picture writing called HIEROGLYPHICS.

Here are some Egyptian picture-letters. There were more than 700 altogether. They must have been difficult to learn!

But they usually went without the letters for a e i o u.

🦅	A		I		Q
	B		K		R
	D		L		S
	F		M		T
	G		N		W
	H		P		Y

Can you work out these words? The first one is done for you.

S K L   School

. . . .

. . . .

. . . .

Try to write some words yourself. Can you write?

M A R Y . . . .   P E T E R . . . .

See how difficult it is!

© History Timelines: Ancient Egypt – J F Nash/Simon & Schuster Education 1993

Background

For numbers the Egyptians used a decimal notation, but had only seven numerals – for 1, 10, 100, 1000, 10 000, 100 000, and 1 million (see opposite). This made computation long and complicated. There was no number higher than a million.

For multiplication they did not do as we do, but used a system of doubling and adding. For example:

$$9 \times 81 : \quad 1 \times 81 = 81$$
$$2 \times 81 = 162$$
$$4 \times 81 = 324$$
$$2 \times 81 = 162$$

(adding these together)

$$9 \times 81 = 729$$

All numbers could be reached in this way, but only multiplying by 10 or 2 was quick.

Division meant doing the same thing backwards:

$$81 \div 9 : \quad 1 \times 9 = 9$$
$$2 \times 9 = 18 \ (\text{so } 3 \times 9 = 27)$$
$$4 \times 9 = 36 \ (\text{so } 7 \times 9 = 63)$$
$$2 \times 9 = 18$$

(adding together again)

$$9 \times 9 = 81 \text{ giving the answer 9}$$

For fractions only 2/3 and 3/4 were the written fractions higher than 1/n; so for example 9/10 was written 1/2 + 1/5 + 1/5.

The Egyptians achieved marvels of architecture using these rather arduous methods of calculation – calculating the height and angle of a pyramid 140 m high without any error, for example: but it is not surprising that they did not make any real advances in mathematical theory and are not known as great or original mathematicians.

Activities

Some Egyptian Mathematics! The point is to draw out how difficult it was using so few symbols, and none for individual digits – hence the invention and widespread use of arabic numerals.

EGYPTIAN NUMBERS

These are the Egyptian numerals

1	10	100	1000	10,000	100,000	1 million

This is how they made numbers

4   27   153

Can you work out these numbers?

Can you add these numbers together and write the answer in Egyptian numerals?

||| + ||||
          |||| = ...

∩ |||| + ∩∩ ||
   ||| ∩∩   = ...

∩∩∩ ||| + ∩∩∩ |||||
∩∩∩ ||| ∩∩∩ ||| = ...

Which do you think is an easier way to do maths — their way or ours?

SOLDIERS AND WEAPONS

Background

Once again the history of weapons shows how reluctant the Egyptians were to change. For 1500 years or more they relied on pretty much the same weapons - spears and sometimes small axes, and bows used by Nubians. When Egypt was conquered and ruled for a while by the Hyksos, around 1500 BC, the Egyptians learned from them to use the light horse-drawn chariot, from which bowmen would shoot at the enemy. This was the first use of wheels in Egyptian transport, and the first time that horses came into common use. The chariot changed battlefield tactics considerably, but the infantry continued to use very much the same weapons as before.

The Egyptians do not seem to have been a warlike people, and refreshingly do not include strength, valour etc. in their lists of ideal qualities. In the Old Kingdom there was no real standing army. It was a peaceful period internally and externally, so there were few soldiers. The Middle Kingdom saw the beginning of soldiers being called up when they were needed, just as men were summoned to help with building or an important expedition.

The New Kingdom was a more warlike period however, and the growing empire needed a large standing army, of about 20,000 men. It was divided into divisions of 5,000 men, each consisting of 25 companies of 200. There were frequent expeditions north into Palestine and Syria, and pharaohs boasted in their funerary wall paintings and writings of the slaughter they caused.

The army was for some the only real means of rising in the world, apart from being a scribe, so may have been quite popular. The navy was not a separate body, but really only acted as a transport and floating base for the army.

✏ Activities

On the sheet are six pictures of soldiers and weapons, numbered only. Some of the weapons were used throughout the period; others came in later, especially during the New Kingdom, when Egypt became warlike and empire-minded.

You could ask children to colour and cut out each picture, write captions against them, and put them on their timelines or in their project books.

The pictures are:

1 Soldier wearing light armour, with spear and shield. Armour did not come in until the New Kingdom, c.1500, but was not used much. The spear and shield were like this from the beginning. Note that the soldier is holding the shield the other way up from soldiers in European history.

2 Round-headed axe. Used up until c.1600 BC. Later replaced by

3 Battle axe. Much more like medieval one, but lighter and with narrower blade.

4 Bow. Used throughout, but until New Kingdom used to be made of two antelope horns joined together. Then became more modern bow made of strips of wood glued or bound together.

5 Scimitar. New Kingdom again. Used all over Asia, and of course by Turks and Saracens at the time of the Crusades.

6 Horse and chariot. Introduced by the Hyksos in c.1500. The chariot held a driver and a bowman, and they dated at the enemy, fired their arrows and darted away again, rather than directly charging.

Soldiers also used daggers, swords and so on, very like medieval ones, throughout the time.

**Attainment targets:
AT1 levels 2,3,4**

SOLDIERS AND WEAPONS

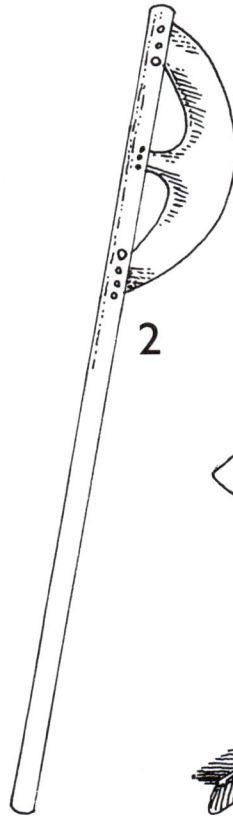

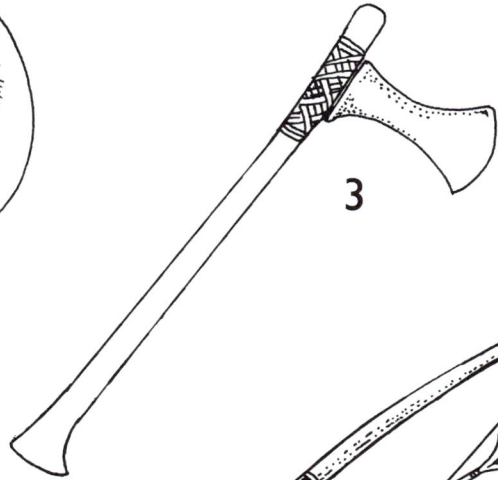

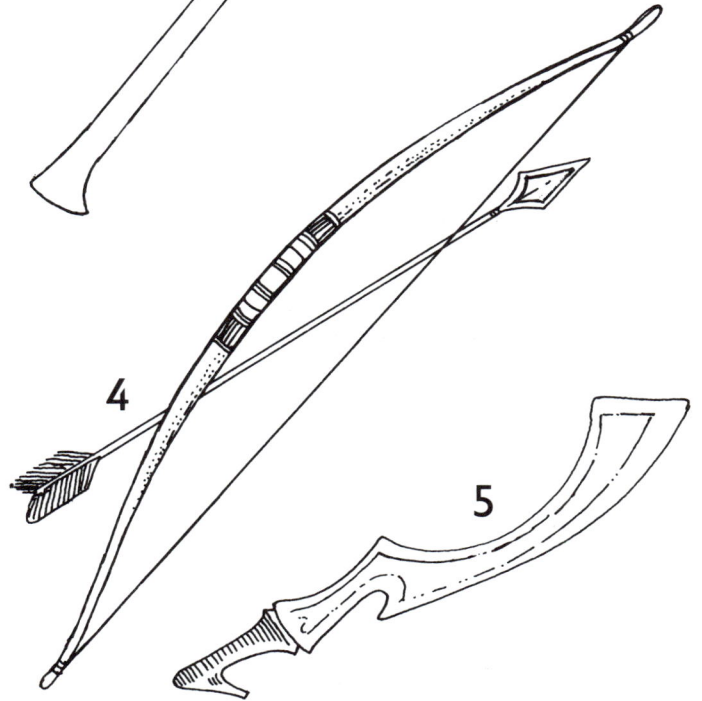

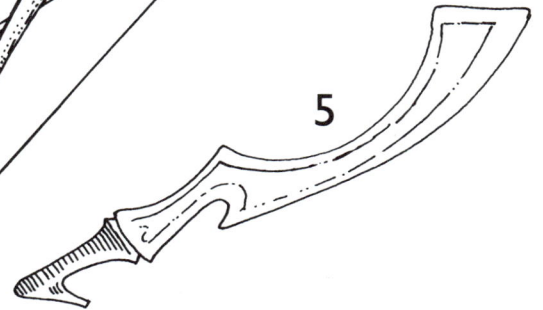

Background

Almost all Egyptian transport was by water, up and down or across the Nile. There were practically no roads. Again the Nile was predictable and beneficent. The current of course flowed north towards the Mediterranean. The wind was nearly always from the north. So if you wished to travel south up the river, you raised your sail; if you wished to go north you lowered it and rowed with the current. Even the Egyptian word for 'sail' was the same as 'go south', and 'downstream' the same as 'go north'.

They never sailed at night, storms were rare, and the main dangers were sandbanks and the shallowness of the river (for this reason boats did not have keels, and had a very shallow draft). Perhaps the lack of variety of Egypt's needs on the water, compared to sea-going peoples with less predictable weather, partly caused the relative lack of development.

But because boats were such a basic part of their lives, model boats were often left in tombs as an essential part of the dead's equipment for the afterlife, and most of what we know comes from these and from pictures in tombs.

Nearly all illustrations are of river-going boats. There are almost none of the sea-going vessels used to fetch timber from Byblos (Lebanon). The Egyptians also built ships on the Red Sea for their expeditions to Punt (Somalia).

The earliest boats were bunches of papyrus reeds lashed together to make simple canoes. People went on using these for thousands of years. In the Old Kingdom they made larger ships with rows of oars and a single, graceful sail; in the Middle Kingdom these were at least 60 m long, with crews of 120. Boats also became specialised – for carrying huge blocks of granite for building, for ceremonies, trading, fishing, pleasure and so on.

Activities

The sheet shows four kinds of boat:

1 Papyrus canoe. Made by binding reeds together. Easy to make and replace, and to use for fishing, hunting, light transport. Used all through period, and on until papyrus stopped growing on the Nile

2 Predynastic vessel (before 3000 BC). Still made of papyrus or reeds, large oar for steering, rectangular sail, oars.

3 Old Kingdom vessel. Made of wood (probably had to be imported), shallow hull, more than one steering oar, two-footed mast, tall sail, oars.

4 New Kingdom. Made of wood (probably had to be imported), shallow hull, more than one steering oar, two-footed mast, tall sail, oars.

Children could write brief descriptions and note changes, and use on time lines or in project books. Points to make: very limited change or advance – why? Because Egyptians were lazy or unimaginative, or because their basic needs did not change much?

**Attainment targets:
AT1 level 3**

EGYPTIAN BOATS

Papyrus Canoe

Early Sailing Boat
Before 3000 BC

Middle Kingdom Boat
1800 BC

New Kingdom Boat
1300 BC

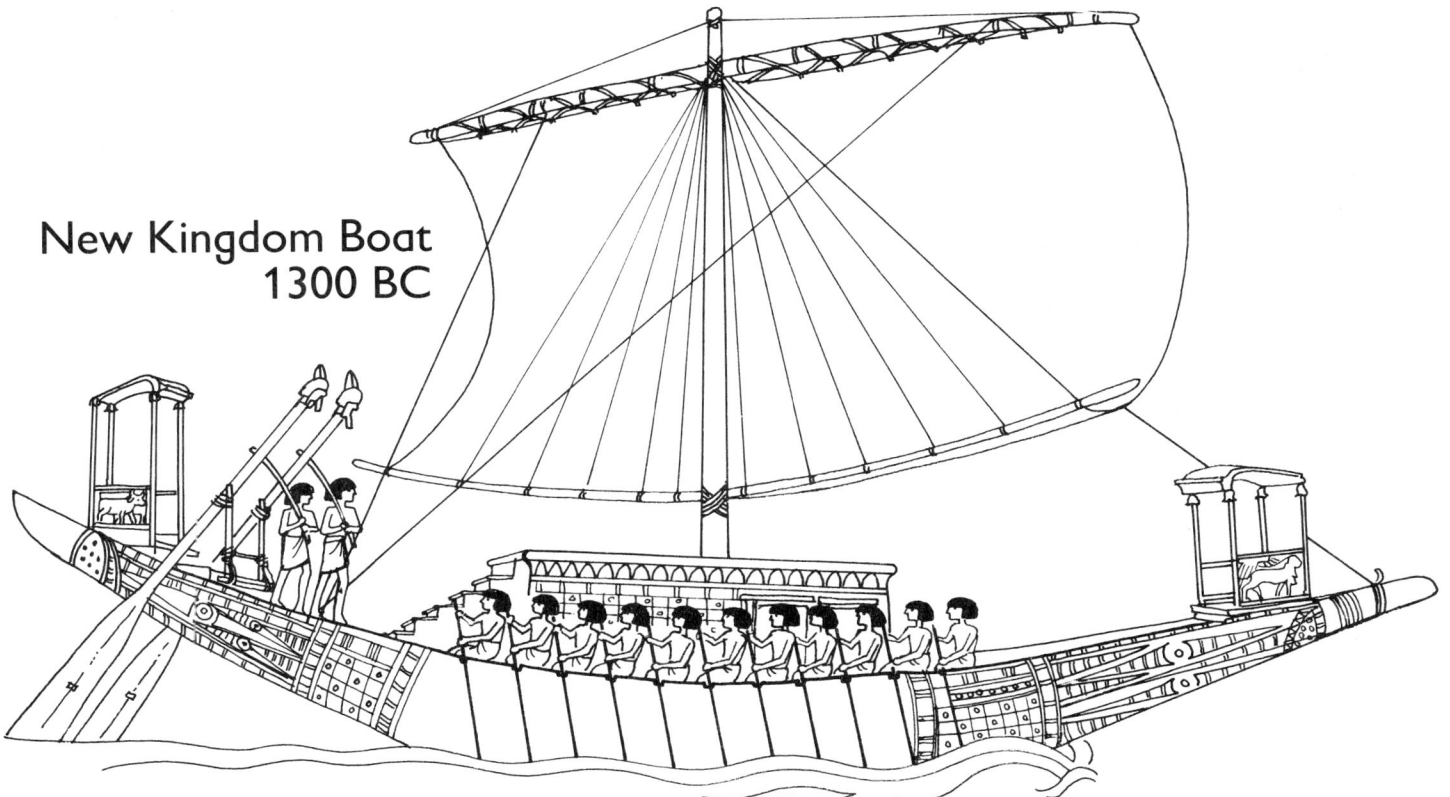

👁 WHO IS THIS MAN? 👁

✏ Activities

This is an exercise of evidence. These articles were found in the tomb of Tutankamun, though the list is very much simplified – there were more than 2000 objects in his tomb, which took archeologists 10 years to clear. I have left out the gold coffins, masks etc and the obscure objects, and left only those which reflect on the dead person's life.

Ideas and hints

He died at 18: why? Either an accident, or murder?

Height: was he quite small, or were people smaller then than now? How does this compare with the tallest children in the class, or the teacher?

Head: we know that priests were clean-shaven, and pharaohs too. The skull was empty because the brain had been removed for embalming. He must have worn ear-rings.

Why were the baby girls there? (They were his still-born daughters.)

The throne shows of course that he was probably a king. He was also a military man, at least in theory. Chariots were not introduced into Egypt until the Hyksos in c. 1600, so this tells us the tomb must have been later than that.

The headrest was used to rest a cushion or pillow on.

Writing things: he was educated (only a few Egyptians knew how to write), or needed them for his scribe?

He must have been fond of games and music.

Why the model boats? (For sailing on the Nile in his afterlife?)

There are no wrong answers here, except for ones which directly contradict the evidence, so the important thing is to speculate freely. Encourage children to make suggestions which use more than one piece of evidence at a time, and ask what other evidence we might like to have to make our guesses better.

**Attainment targets:
AT2 level 4; AT3 levels 2,3,4**

👁 WHO IS THIS MAN? 👁

You are an archaeologist. You discover an Egyptian tomb. In it is a mummy, together with some things that have been put there with him. You undo the mummy and find the remains of the body.

Your job is to work out as much as possible about the man whose body you have found.

THE BODY

Age: 18 (worked out from his bones)
Sex: male
Height: 1.68 m
Head: clean shaven
Skull: empty, sign of a heavy blow on one side
Earlobes: pierced
Eyelashes: very long

The bodies of 2 baby girls are in the tomb with the man.

THE OBJECTS

a chariot
bows and shields
sticks and whips
a throne
a bed
a headrest
chairs and stools
boxes
clothes
gloves
sandals
writing things
board games
jewelry
fans made of ostrich feathers
musical instruments
model boats

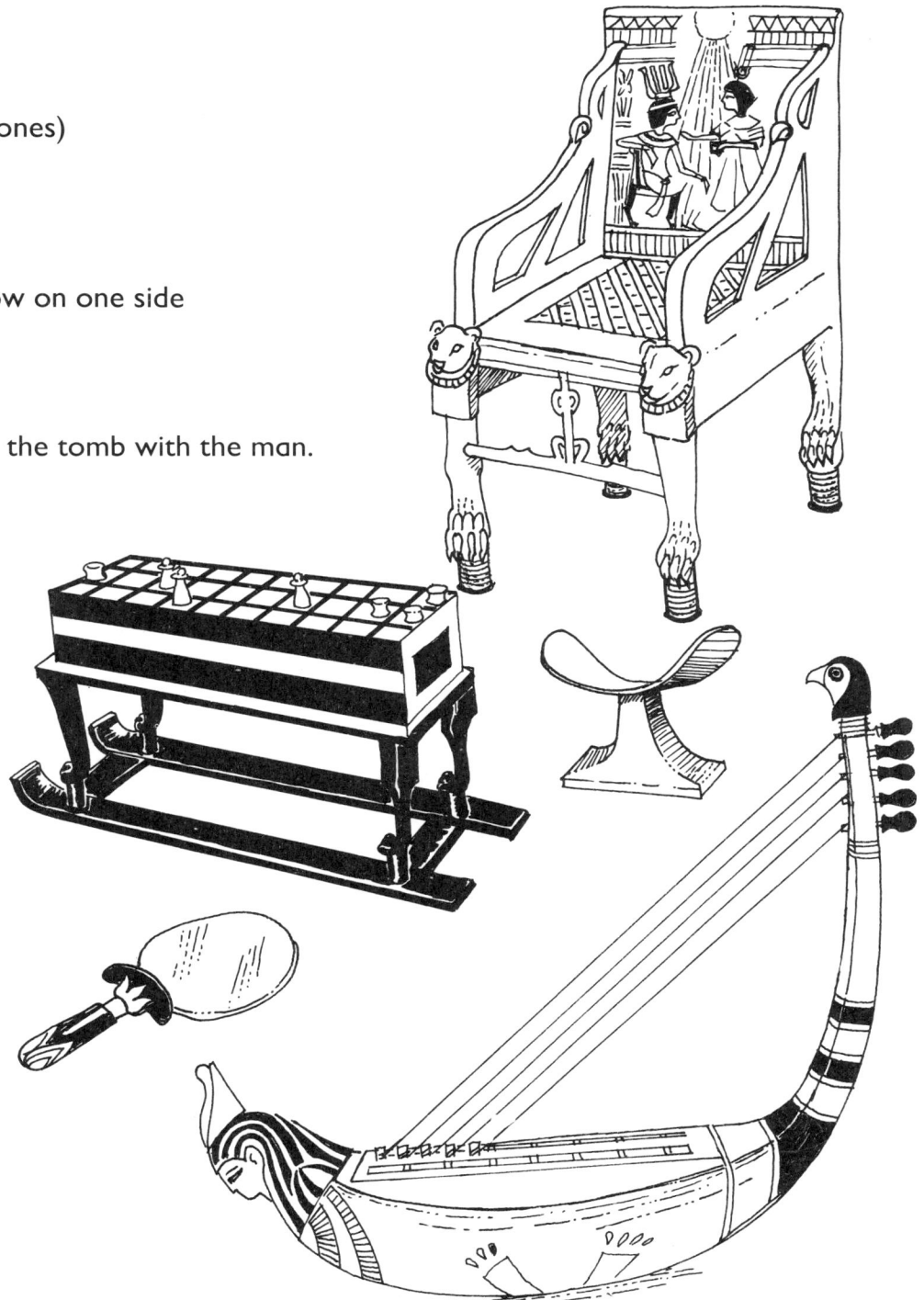

FINDING OUT FROM PICTURES

✏️ *Activities*

This activity is intended to

▲ help to show how we know about Ancient Egypt.

▲ develop the skill of looking carefully at pictures and other evidence – it is all too easy to glance at something without really working out what it tells us.

Picture 1 shows men plucking geese. Notice where the scene takes place (in a hut?), what the men are sitting on and what they are wearing. It was unusual for Egyptians to have long hair and beards; perhaps these are foreigners or slaves.

Picture 2 shows two men picking grapes. Notice their hair and what they are collecting their grapes in.

Picture 3 shows stone amsons at work, using hammer and chisel and a ruler.

Picture 4 shows female musicians playing (l. to r.) a harp, lute, flutes and lyre.

Attainment targets:
AT3 levels, 2,3

FINDING OUT FROM PICTURES

Egyptians drew lots of pictures in their tombs. They tell us all sorts of things about their lives.

Look at these pictures and write something about each one. Say what you think is going on; what the people are doing and why; anything else you think is interesting about the picture.

3

4

EGYPT AND THE ANCIENT WORLD

BACKGROUND

Until at least the end of the New Kingdom all international trade was directed by the Pharaoh. There were four main kinds of trade: first (not really trade since it was taken as of right), expeditions to get copper and turquoise from the mines of Sinai; second, south up the Nile to Nubia for ebony, ivory, animals and animal skins and so on (this was a combination of genuine trade and extortion); third, fleets of ships, up to 40 at a time, to fetch timber, especially cedar, from Byblos and the forests of Lebanon (Egypt was very short of wood and this supply was essential for their building projects); and last, occasional expeditions down the Red Sea coast to Punt (Ethiopia or Somalia) for myrrh, resins and other African exotica.

In exchange the Egyptians exported gold – there were large deposits of gold in the hills to the east of the Nile – grain, of which they probably had a surplus in many years, papyrus and cloth.

There must also have been exchanges with the Greek islands, if not trade. Cretan and Mycenean pottery has been found in Egypt, and there are pictures in tombs of 'princes of Crete' with gifts. In the Late Period Greeks were allowed to set up trading stations in the Delta, such as Naukritis.

But Egypt probably learned most from the great civilisation of Mesopotamia, though earlier on when the country was not yet unified. They learned building techniques – how to make mud bricks instead of wattle and daub; architecture – pillars and pilasters; and most important of all, writing – though they took the Asian idea of writing and invented the hieroglyphic system on their own.

Activities

A base map of the Eastern Mediterranean, showing the main places and peoples the Egyptians had to do with. The map shows the greatest extent of the Egyptian Empire.

Use the map

▲ as background information

▲ for map work on scale and distance

▲ for labelling trade routes and raw materials. Children could colour the map to show the sea, the Egyptian Empire, the other peoples.

Attainment targets:
AT1
Geography AT1 levels 3,4

EGYPT AND
THE ANCIENT WORLD

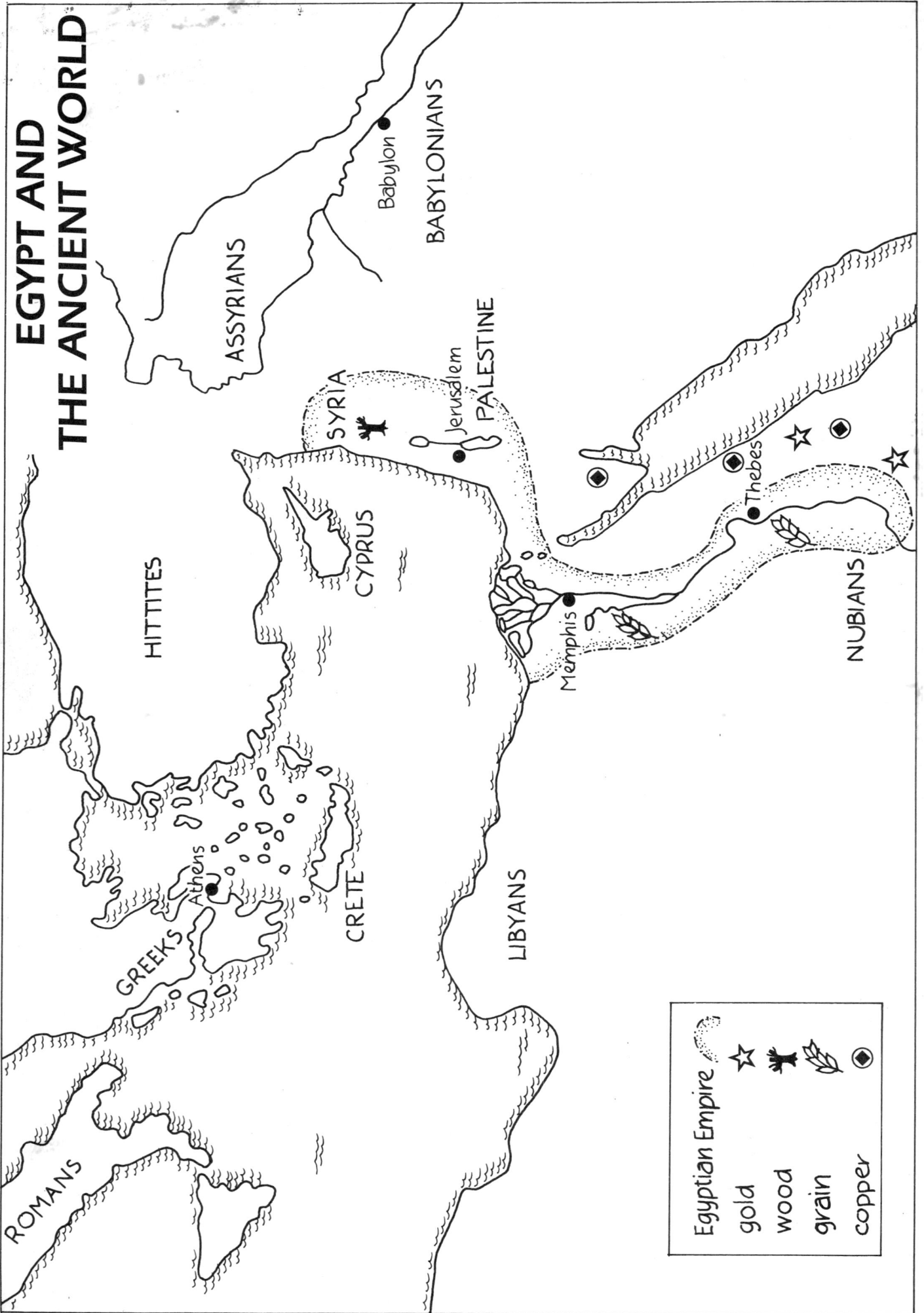

ASSYRIANS

BABYLONIANS

Babylon

SYRIA

Jerusalem

PALESTINE

CYPRUS

HITTITES

Memphis

Thebes

NUBIANS

CRETE

Athens

GREEKS

LIBYANS

ROMANS

| Egyptian Empire | ☆ gold | ✦ wood | 🌾 grain | ◉ copper |